MINING
OIL & GAS
EXPLAINED

Oil pumping unit — Western Canada.

Photo courtesy of Francana Oil & Gas Limited.

Denison's No. 2 shaft complex.

Photo courtesy of Denison Mines Limited.

Published by

NORTHERN MINER PRESS LIMITED

7 Labatt Avenue, Toronto, Canada   M5A 3P2

1st printing April, 1979
2nd printing April, 1981
3rd printing December, 1982

Copyright 1979 by Northern Miner Press Limited
ISBN 0-919336-02-7

Contents

Foreword

This book is not intended as a textbook, but has been developed for the non-technical reader. The mining and oil industries are complex, varied and highly technical businesses, and there is a general need on the part of many people for descriptions in lay terms that will provide some basic understanding and visual concept of these operations. Both are highly visible industries. Almost everyone makes use of motor transport at one time or another, and the operating mines and oil companies are customers of virtually every Canadian manufacturer, service industry and major supply house.

About 250,000 Canadians are shareholders in Canadian mining and exploration companies, and mining provides employment directly and indirectly for 9% of Canada's labor force. In one way or another, the products of our mines touch on the daily lives of each one of us. This is equally true of oil and gas, which also come into direct contact with many people in the heating of their homes or the cooking of their food. Thus, there are a great many people who may wish to broaden their basic knowledge and acquire understanding of these industries — students, office workers in the firms doing business with the

mining, oil and gas companies, and the layman who seeks to develop a more intelligent appreciation of his country's natural resources.

For a number of years this void was filled by the book, Mining Explained, produced by The Northern Miner, a weekly publication which has covered the Canadian mining scene for over 65 years. Some of these chapters, which were prepared by authorities on various aspects of the mining business, have been retained in the present volume, after thorough revision and updating.

Much of the editing and writing of the earlier book were done by Maurice R. Brown, Editor of The Northern Miner. Later revisions were incorporated by the late H. R. Rice, Professor Emeritus of Mining Engineering, University of Toronto, who was responsible for rewriting the mining sections, including new chapters on the mining scene and environmental concerns.

Among others, experts advice and assistance were offered by Dave Marshall, Heath & Sherwood Drilling; Peter M. D. Bradshaw, vice-president, Barringer Magenta Ltd.; Dr. Robbert A. Bosschart, consulting geophysicist; and The Mining Association of Canada. We are indebted to Inco Limited for the use of several sketches illustrating stoping methods from their book, "The Winning of Nickel".

The chapters on the petroleum industry have been prepared by Dr. J. E. F. DeWeil, Consulting Geologist, Calgary, Alberta. Dr. DeWeil is well known for his interpretive comments on the petroleum industry through his column "Oil and Gas Highlights for the Mining Man" which appeared in The Northern Miner for a number of years.

Northern Miner Press Limited

The Millenbach shaft and concentrator of the Lake Dufault Division of Corporation Falconbridge Copper, in Northwestern Quebec, are shown at right. The copper concentrates are trucked to the nearby Noranda smelter.

The Giant Yellowknife gold mine, one of the Falconbridge group, is located on the north shore of Great Slave Lake, N.W.T. Seen here are the headframe over the main shaft, the mill, shops and roaster.
Photos by George Hunter

Geologists examine drill core at Texasgulf prospect in northern Canada.

CHAPTER I

The Mining Scene

There are more than seven thousand producing mines in the world, and from them come the raw materials for most of our industry, and most of the energy on which our society is so dependent. Those seven thousand do not include oil or gas wells, but are the ones which mine the ores of metals, produce raw materials for our chemical industries, building materials, coal and uranium for energy, and such useful though unsung items as the sizing in the paper on which this is printed. Incidental to this, the reader is challenged to follow his or her activities through a normal day, and to try to find a single moment in which he or she is not concerned somehow with a mineral substance or derivative.

Among those seven thousand mines there are no two that are quite alike. They vary in size from the huge open pit copper mines such as at Bingham Canyon, Utah, U.S.A. where several hundred thousand tonnes of copper ore are mined and milled each day, down to small operations turning out a few scores, or even dozens of tonnes. Again, whatever their sizes, or whatever their products, no two will be found to be quite alike.

The search for metals, precious stones, and other minerals has provided the real roots for great events in history — ancient and modern — and has therefore determined much of our economic geography and demography. Romance is there, too, for the principal concomitant of man's mining world has always been adventure. The oldest map ever found in the world is believed to be a plan of an ancient Egyptian gold mine, and somehow this does not seem to be an accident. We could follow the voyages of the Argos in the quest for the "golden fleece" — really sheepskins used by the tribes near the eastern end of the Black Sea to collect gold from placer washings — and trace a strong thread through all subsequent human history. Our own Canadian history and geography have been very much influenced by exploration for minerals.

Coal is widespread in the world, and the great industrial nations are those which took early advantage of their resources to supply energy, and chemical raw materials for their factories and transport systems. While we are not going to be much concerned with coal in this small book, the foregoing is one of the great political facts of life. The great industrial nations also have varying amounts of metallic ores; those that

Figure I-1 — Drill hole radiometric logging system to determine grade of uranium deposit in Greenland.

have them in abundance are fortunate, and those who are less so have become traders and manufacturers, with their own coal providing the necessary energy base.

Beginning with the United States, there are the great copper camps of Montana, Utah, Arizona, New Mexico and other western states. The lead and zinc of the tri-state area centred in Missouri have long been famous. There are uranium ores in New Mexico and Wyoming, iron ores in the ranges of Minnesota, Wisconsin and Michigan, elemental sulphur in the Gulf states, salt in the states bordering on the Great Lakes, silver in Idaho and Nevada. And, of course, there are reserves of coal in many states. The modern petroleum industry had its start in Pennsylvania, unless one wishes to allow that distinction to Ontario in Canada. Space forbids a more complete inventory of United States mineral resources, but they are very considerable, varied, and of great economic import.

Latin America's history has been shaped by minerals perhaps to a greater extent than that of any other region in the past few centuries. Mexico is well known as an important producer of silver, lead, copper and zinc. In South America, there are some of the world's greatest copper mines in Chile and Peru; Bolivia is famous among mining folk for its tin. Brazil has an ancient gold mining area in Minas Gerais, and the northern part of the continent has great reserves of high quality iron ore.

South Africa has the famous Witwatersrand gold area, leading the world in the production of that precious metal, about 70 per cent of the non-communist total. Its producers include one mine, the Western Deep Levels, which has been developed to a depth of 3½ kilometres vertically below surface. There are also the old and famous diamond fields at Kimberley, and the alluvial diamond workings along the Atlantic near the mouths of the

Orange and Vaal Rivers. South Africa also produces important quantities of manganese. In central Africa there are the chrome and asbestos mines of Rhodesia (or Zimbabwe), and the great copper belts of Zambia and Zaire. All have formed important bases for the economic and social structures of the continent.

In India, there is the gold field at Kolar in the south, where development and mining are carried out at depths greater than three kilometres. Though not now as important as they were in terms of production, this area has contributed significantly to techniques of mining at great depths. India also has large reserves of high quality iron ore, and is heavily engaged in exploration designed to expand the production of other metals, notably copper, lead and zinc. It has long been an important source of manganese.

India's history is replete with mining lore, and Golconda is practically synonomous with diamonds. The reader may be interested to know that the famous "Damascus" swords were made from an iron produced in India which was an important item of commerce for many years in ancient times.

China has for a long time been the world's leading producer of tungsten. She has immense coal reserves under development, and is also actively developing deposits of copper, iron, and other metals.

Japan has reserves of coal, but lacks an abundance of metals. She is, therefore, illustrative of a point made earlier in that she has applied her industriousness to her coal to establish an important place among the world's manufacturing and trading nations.

Russia's mineral resources are vast, with immense reserves of iron ore and coal, and most of the other metals needed for a self-sufficient economy. From Siberia, she produces enough gold to make her second only to South Africa, as well as turning out important quantities of platinum, and even industrial-grade diamonds. The Urals include one of the world's great mineralogical provinces, and there are great iron ore fields in the Ukraine. Asbestos, chrome, and manganese are also abundant.

Continental Europe and Great Britain contain many historical metal mining fields which continue to produce. Iron ore is fairly common in continental Europe, and especially so in Sweden where production of iron ore per capita is among the highest in the world. The historic areas of Saxony and Silesia in eastern Europe, and the tin fields of Cornwall in England are literally cradles of the technologies of mining, ore dressing, and smelting.

The countries of the Mediterranean basin have had their histories shaped from the earliest times by their minerals and its trades. The Greeks financed their wars with the Persians largely with silver produced at Laurium, and the Romans produced copper at Rio Tinto, an area which is still in operation. The Phoenicians carried on much of this trade, and went as far as Cornwall for tin.

Figure I-2 — Cominco operates and holds substantial interest in Binani zinc smelter and sulphuric acid plant in India.

The above has been a quick look at the world of metals and minerals, and it is by no means complete. But one of our purposes is to arouse curiosity, and something of an awareness of minerals in human affairs.

On the Canadian scene, we have one of the leading mineral producing and trading countries of the world. Including fuels, metals, structural materials and non-metallic or industrial minerals, our industries turn out more than sixty items of statistical account, with total values well above $32 billion. The mineral sector is the first ranked earner of foreign exchange among all industries, earning about $5.5 billion as net surplus.

The production of primary metals, industrial minerals, and structural minerals runs to more than $13 billion. Including processing and fabricating, this value exceeds $27 billion. The productive mineral industries employ over 170,000 people in exploration, mining, extraction, smelting and refining, and through multiplier effects contribute to the livelihoods of over a million Canadians. About 250,000 Canadians enjoy dividends paid by mining companies.

In the decade to 1990, according to a forecast of Energy Mines and Resources Canada, real production of the non-fuel mineral industry will grow at an annual average rate of 2.5%; exports at 2.8% in real terms; employment by an average of 1.1% per year. Total capital investment is forecast at $42 billion to 1990.

Canada's mine production of copper was fourth in the world. In other metals, we were third in lead,

first in zinc, first in nickel, third in gold, and second in silver. We were also first in asbestos, and second in potash.

In the production of metals and coal from Canada's mines, about 600 million tonnes of ore and waste rock are mined each year from a total of about two hundred underground and open pit mines. In a crushed state, this would occupy a conical pile about one kilometre in diameter, and a half kilometre high. Of the two hundred mines mentioned, over forty produce 5,000 tons or more of ore per day.

Canada has several mining areas which are world famous. Although mining for gold and iron ore was carried on from early colonial days, the real economic take-off was the discovery of the rich silver veins at Cobalt shortly after the turn of this century. This "grass-roots" camp generated the capital and incentive for the discovery and development of the great gold fields of Porcupine and Kirkland Lake, which have now lost most of their economic import. In their turn, however, they fostered the copper mines of Rouyn-Noranda, Flin Flon in Manitoba, gold in the Northwest Territories, uranium and radium at Great Bear Lake, and several others. The Gaspé Copper mines, the Quebec-Labrador iron fields, much of the potash developments in Saskatchewan, and other mining enterprise, can be said to be direct financial descendents in the third and fourth generation of that Cobalt camp, even though its productive significance has long since ceased.

Contemporarily with Cobalt, the great nickel-copper deposits of the

Figure I-3 — Inco's Thompson mine and smelter in Northern Manitoba, with part of the city of Thompson in the background.

Sudbury area were opened up, though they were actually discovered during the advance of the Canadian Pacific Railway through that country during the 1880s. Sudbury is now the largest single source of nickel in the world, as well as being important in copper, industrial sulphur, and platinum metals. At Inco's Creighton mine there is the deepest continuous shaft in the western world, its bottom being 2,176 meters below surface.

At Kimberley, in British Columbia, Cominco's great Sullivan Mine is famous as containing the world's largest single orebody of lead, zinc, and silver. It, too, has offspring in other mining areas and in other industry, notably in the manufacture of fertilizers. The company gave birth to a remarkable technique of mineral dressing, to be referred to in a later chapter, without which this great resource could not have been profitable. In British Columbia, too, we have great open pit copper mines such as Lornex, Bethlehem, and others of a type referred to as "porphyry" deposits, and similar to some of the great mines of the southwestern United States. Northern British Columbia also produces important quantities of high quality asbestos.

All Canadian provinces include at least some mineral production or activity, and in addition to those which have been mentioned however briefly above, we have nickel, copper and zinc in Manitoba; copper, zinc and lead in New Brunswick, asbestos in Quebec and Newfoundland, and various base metals and industrial minerals in Nova Scotia. Saskatchewan is developing as a leading uranium producer. Even Prince Edward Island produces a share of an important industrial mineral — gravel.

The technology of Canadian mining is of first quality, and in the exchange of technical expertise, our industry bears its full share. It has pioneered in certain mining methods, a number of metallurgical processes, and mineral dressing techniques, which have been adopted elsewhere in the world, so that we are by no means a net importer of technology. Some of our mines have been developed to great depths, in the order of 2,400 meters at McIntyre in Porcupine, and at Lake Shore and Wright-Hargreaves in Kirkland Lake. Such depths require high expertise in the support of ground under the pressures encountered, and other mines benefit from the techniques developed.

The reader will note numerous references and examples which are associated with the geology and technologies of gold mining. Gold mining in Canada has lost much of its importance but mining and exploration geology, and mining and milling techniques still owe much of their levels of expertise to the search for, and production of, gold twenty and more years ago. And, in most cases, the principles described are equally applicable to other branches of mining.

As far as convenient, quantitative data are presented in metric or "S.I." units, even though the conversion is not expected to be complete in Canada and other western countries for several years. In some discussions Imperial units will be retained, as certain terms will not likely fall out of use for some time to come. But, for reference purposes, a simple conversion table is included for the convenience of those who may have calculations of their own to make.

Figure I-4 — An apprentice learns welding techniques at Bougainville Copper in Papua New Guinea.

Conversion Table

Metric — Imperial: Imperial — Metric

Area

1 hectare = 2.4710 acres
= 10000 square meters

1 acre = 0.4047 hectares

1 square kilometer = 0.3861 square miles
= 247.1 acres
= 100 hectares

1 square mile = 640 acres
= 2.59 square kilometers
= 258.99 hectares

1 square foot = 0.0929 square meters
= 929.03 square centimeters

1 square meter = 10.7638 square feet
= 10000 square centimeters

1 square centimeter = 0.155 square inches

1 square inch = 6.4516 square centimeters
= 645.16 square millimeters

Weight

(1 metric ton = 1 tonne)

1 metric ton = 1000 kilograms
= 2204.6 pounds
= 1.1023 short tons

1 long ton = 2240 pounds
= 1.016 metric tons or tonnes
= 1016.4 kilograms

1 short ton = 2000 pounds
= 0.9071 tonnes
= 907.8 kilograms

1 kilogram = 2.2046 pounds
= 1000 grams

1 ounce troy = 31.103 grams

1 ounce avoirdupois = 28.3495 grams

Length

1 meter = 3.281 feet
= 39.37 inches

1 foot = 0.305 meters

1 kilometer = 3281 feet
= 0.621 miles

1 mile = 1609.3 meters
= 1.6093 kilometers

1 centimeter = 0.3937 inches

1 inch = 2.54 centimeters
= 25.4 millimeters

Volume

1 litre = 1000 cubic centimeters
= 61.025 cubic inches
= 0.220 imperial gallons

1 imperial gallon = 4.546 litres
= 4546 cubic centimeters

Assaying, Sampling, Marketing

1 troy ounce/short ton = 34.2857 grams per tonne

1 troy ounce-foot = 10.45 grams-meters

1% (metal) -foot = 0.3048 %-meters
= 30.48 %-centimeters

1 metric ton unit = 1% x 1000 kilograms
= 10 kilograms
= 22.046 pounds

1 long ton unit = 1% x 1 long ton
= 22.4 pounds
= 10.16 kilograms

1 short ton unit = 1% x 2000 pounds
= 20 pounds
= 9.072 kilograms

CHAPTER II

Elementary Geology

"Geology" is a very broad term which means, literally, "the study of the earth." It has many branches, each of which has a number of esoteric specializations. The ones with which we are concerned here involve the description of the physical and chemical processes by which rock structures have been formed. This includes occurrences which in certain circumstances may be referred to as "orebodies," that is when minerals or suites of minerals are present in economic quantity and quality. To put it another way, it is ore when the minerals are present in sufficient quantity to provide adequate grade and tonnage for economic recovery.

Mineral discovery is largely a result of bringing together a number of geology's sub-disciplines, in order to converge on a valuable mineral deposit — if one be present. These sub-disciplines are many, and in constant process of development. As an example, the reader will have noted that in recent years the popular scientific press has given a great deal of attention to "continental drift," and he should not be surprised to learn that the exploration geologist has its possible manifestations very much in mind when making his deductions on regional scales.

Some knowledge of geology is necessary both in seeking out and in understanding the habits of orebodies. This understanding, to a varying degree, is a necessity, not only to the geologist but to the geophysicst, mining engineer, prospector, and to the layman who may wish to invest in mining companies.

Indeed, a knowledge of geology, even to the most elementary degree, can be of invaluable help to the layman — the investor who "puts his money in the ground". For instance, he might some day benefit from his knowledge, say, that low temperature mineral deposits (for example most silver orebodies) change rather quickly with depth, or that post-ore faulting can play havoc with an orebody.

The average individual who is interested enough in mining to want to read this book probably has at least some knowledge of the business, but knows little or nothing about geology. He will read a report on a mining company avidly, particularly that portion which deals with the financial aspects, but he will barely skim over the section dealing with the geological features of the company's property. He is overawed, perhaps, by the strange words and terms that the geologist uses so profusely in his attempts to describe and to evaluate the character and the processes by which the orebodies have been formed.

While a full understanding of **geology, mineralogy** and **petrography,** the sciences of the earth, minerals and rocks, respectively, is essential to the geologist, this chapter will attempt to explain and outline only the barest fundamentals of these subjects, while at the same time endeavoring to familiarize the reader with the common terms used in the every day business of mining. In the next chapter, some of the economic aspects of geology will be treated in a similar manner.

Earth Over Four Billion Years Old

As mentioned, geology is the study of the earth. Without delving into the fascinating realms of historical geology, but before looking at the composition of the earth, it might be well to point out that our earth is very, very old indeed. In fact, the oldest recognized rocks probably date back 4,000,000,000 years and more. This is an immense period of time, but the geologist must think of time in terms that seem to us almost immeasurably great.

It requires a great deal of time to complete geological processes and cycles, such as the lifting up of mountain ranges and their subsequent wearing away by the slow processes of erosion. And there have been many such cycles, which the geologist calls **eras.** Periods of mountain building are referred to as

revolutions, a relatively recent one giving us the Rockies and other western mountain ranges. Just as in the history of man, the earth has experienced long periods of relatively peaceful existence. But from time to time, these great disturbances which take place within its crust literally change the face of our planet.

But what of the earth itself as we know it today, the earth that is slowly giving up its vast mineral wealth and secrets and in so doing, raising our standard of living?

The earth is made up of a host of elements, of which the most abundant, in order, are oxygen, silicon, aluminum, iron and calcium. A few of the elements — such as gold, silver and copper — occur as pure metal, but most have joined with other elements to form the various rocks and minerals that comprise the earth. For instance, iron and sulphur combine in a definite ratio to form **pyrite,** a common mineral well known to the prospector.

Rocks and Minerals

What is the difference between a rock and a mineral? A **mineral** may be defined as a naturally occurring homogenous substance having definite physical properties and chemical composition and, if formed under favorable conditions, a definite crystal form. A **rock,** on the other hand, is simply a combination of minerals.

Most minerals, like most rocks, are valueless from an economic standpoint.

Minerals can often be readily recognized by their appearance and

Figure II-1 — Theano Point, east shore of Lake Superior, scene of Canada's probably first uranium discovery, rediscovered a century later.

can be specifically identified by their various and particular characteristic physical properties. But the exact identification of rocks is frequently more difficult, for usually they cannot be readily and specifically identified by any series of simple tests. However, all rocks fall into three general classifications — igneous, sedimentary and metamorphic — and as such can be identified by direct observation after only a little experience.

Igneous Rocks From Molten Material

Igneous rocks, as the name implies, are those that have been formed by the cooling and consequent solidification of a once hot and fluid mass known as a **magma.** This results in the crystals of the different minerals being interlocked, which is one of the distinguishing features of igneous rocks.

All igneous rocks originate at great depth in the earth's crust, where both temperature and pressure must be very high. When any opportunity permits, therefore, these rocks will expand and tend to flow towards surface, though they may cool and solidify on the way. Rocks that cool at depth are referred to as **plutonic.** And because they cool slowly, their crystals have plenty of time to grow and so are coarse grained. This is known as a **granular** or **granitic texture.**

Rock that comes closer to surface will cool a little faster, so the crystals will have less chance to grow, resulting in a finer grained rock. Still other molten magma may reach surface and run out or extrude as lava flows. Such magma would cool quickly, giving the crystals little chance to form, resulting in a fine grained or **volcanic** type of rock.

Solid rock, magma or gaseous matter may erupt from a vent in the earth with explosive force, when it is known as a **volcano.** While there were numerous volcanoes in Canada during early geologic time, these have long since become extinct. There are no active volcanoes in this country at the present time, though there are some in Alaska.

Some of our early volcanoes must have been awe-inspiring sights indeed, for they ejected amazing amounts of lava (Fig. II-4). In what the geologist refers to as Keweenawan time, for instance (many millions of years ago), a thickness of some 6,000 meters of lava poured from volcanoes and fissures in the Lake Superior region.

The solid material ejected from volcanoes varies from fine dust to rock fragments weighing hundreds of tons. This material was once solid rock from around the crater, or at least a semi-viscous mass that had partially cooled, and which was subsequently blown to pieces by exploding gases. Larger angular pieces form what is known as **agglomerate** or **volcanic breccia,** while the finer materials consolidate into a rock called **tuff.**

The haphazard arrangement of the angular rock fragments in breccias gives rise to numerous openings that permit the entry of mineral bearing solutions and so, as we will see in the subsequent chapter, form a rock family that is of some economic signficance.

And just as the different structural features result in different types of igneous rocks, the variable compositions of the original magma result in a wide variation in composition for this rock group. For instance, if the magma were acid in

Figure II-2 — Porphyritic granite showing phenocrysts of lighter colored feldspar, near Rossport, Ontario.

Figure II-3 — Amygdaloidal lava showing vesicles or gas cavities filled with later minerals.

either brown mica known as **biotite** or black **hornblende.** If any granite is observed closely, there should be no difficulty in seeing the actual crystal forms that these minerals take, for granites are usually medium to coarse grained (Fig. II-2).

Granite, being a highly resistant rock, frequently forms prominent landscape features. For the same reason, it is frequently quarried for monumental and building stone.

Syenite is the name of a somewhat similar igneous rock, but contains less silica and is described as an intermediate rock. It is much less widespread than granite.

character — that is, contained a high percentage of silica — the resulting rock would contain an abundance of quartz and so would be light in color. On the other hand, if the magma had a lower silica content, that is, it was more basic, the resulting rock would have less silica and would be composed of darker colored minerals.

Igneous rocks are very common, particularly in what is known as the Canadian Precambrian Shield, and in reality are the origin of all rocks. Let us, therefore, mention some of the more common specific members of this big and important family of igneous rocks, and note their chief distinguishing characteristics.

Perhaps the most common igneous rock of all is granite. And while there are many varieties, all are formed from acidic (siliceous) magmas and so, as already noted, tend to show in light shades of colors, that is, pinks to grays.

Granites consist chiefly of quartz and a feldspar mineral, together with

Figure II-4 — Pillow lava in greenstone, near Jackfish, Northern Ontario. The pillows are formed at the edge of the onward moving lava flow as the crust cools and is tumbled into big balls, or pillows, the centre of which cools and solidifies more gradually.

Figure II-5 — Pegmatite dike cutting gneiss, Highway 7, just east of Arden, Ontario.

Granite No Longer Frowned On

For many years it was thought that granites were unfavorable host rocks for ore deposition. That view was justified when considering the great areas of the Precambrian Shield that are customarily colored pink and denote vast quantities of acidic magma that welled up during the relatively late years of geological pre-history. There are, however, older granites in which ores of gold and uranium have been found and profitably exploited, and these granitic types are found as constituent members of the greenstone areas which will be referred to a little later. Examples include uranium near Lake Athabaska, and gold in the Missinaibi area of Ontario. Indeed, the host rock of the famous Kirkland Lake gold mining area in northern Ontario is syenite, a close relative of granite.

Rhyolite is the name given to an extrusive igneous rock of the same general composition as granite, but which has cooled so quickly that the crystals are too fine to be identified. The Horne mine, the original property of Noranda Mines, is associated with these rocks.

Many Basic Igneous Rocks

Turning to the darker colored or more basic igneous rocks, one of the commonest is **diorite.** It contains little or no quartz, consisting chiefly of feldspar and some dark basic material such as biotite (mica), hornblende or pyroxene. Although much darker than granite, diorite has similar texture and occurrences. **Gabbro,** which contains even less silica, is still darker in color than diorite, though closely related. **Norite,** a specific rock of the gabbro family, is host to the rich nickel deposits of the Sudbury area of Ontario.

Figure II-6 — A small dike seen on Highway 144, a few miles south of Gogama, Ontario.

A finer grained sister to gabbro is **diabase,** while **basalt** is lava that has solidified quickly, forming a black rock with crystals of only microscopic size. The orebodies at the San Antonio gold mine in Manitoba were found in diabase.

Rock made up wholly of dark ferromagnesian minerals is known as **peridotite.** Most chromium deposits are found in rocks of this group. Peridotites themselves alter readily to **serpentines,** which in turn are host rocks for asbestos deposits.

An igneous rock that contains distinct crystals imbedded in a much finer grained groundmass is called **porphyry,** a name which applies to this characteristic texture, rather than to any particular rock species. Many of our gold deposits occur in porphryries, for example the MacLeod mine at Geraldton, Ont. Some copper deposits such as the Bethlehem orebodies in the Highland Valley, B.C., occur in rocks that are porphyritic in texture.

Sedimentary Rocks Formed Under Water

Sedimentary rocks, the second of the three main divisions, are those that have been laid down under water, in the ever constant process of erosion. (Niagara Falls is backing up at the rate of over a foot a year, the eroded material from which is settling on the bottom of Lake Ontario to ultimately — millions of years hence — consolidate into a sedimentary rock.) Assisted by such processes as pressure, the worn or weathered rock particles are ultimately solidified or knitted together into a solid rock mass.

Rocks of the sedimentary family are characterized by bedding (Fig. III-3). That is, it is frequently possible to see layers as they were

Figure II-7 — Conglomerate composed largely of quartz pebbles, Elliot Lake, Ontario.

a common sedimentary rock representing the consolidation of sand. Gravel beds that have been solidified clearly show the water-worn pebbles and are known as **conglomerates** (Fig. II-7). The uranium deposits of the Elliot Lake area in Ontario are apparently confined to conglomerate beds. These dip rather gently, but persist to considerable depths.

Most readers are likewise familiar with **clay,** which is argillaceous material that retains enough moisture to be plastic. Through the loss of this water, as well as other changes, clays may eventually be transformed into **shale.** Though a solid rock, shale will readily split or part along the original laminations or planes along which the material was laid down.

actually laid down — the coarser particles forming a distinct band and finer particles forming progressively higher bands or beds. But the individual particles do not show the interlocking that features igneous rocks, and are actually cemented together.

It should be noted that in the long ages of geologic time, all parts of the earth's surface were, at one time or another, covered by great seas. So sedimentary rocks can occur anywhere. It should be noted, too, that through subsequent distortion of the earth's crust, the once horizontal sedimentary beds may be folded into any position (Fig. II-8), and actually sometimes are found standing vertically. Indeed, they could be thrown right over, with the coarser beds that obviously must have been the first to settle on the lake bed lying on top of the finer beds.

What are some of the more common sedimentary rocks? Most readers are familiar with **sandstone** as used in the building trade. This is

Limestone is another common sedimentary rock, but one which has a somewhat different origin. As rocks were eroded, washed by rain into the rivers, and eventually carried out to sea, much of the calcium carbonate (lime) of the original rocks became dissolved in

Figure II-8 — Banded iron formation at Sherman mine, Northern Ontario.

Figure II-9 — Garnet crystal, about 18 mm diameter, embedded in quartz.

the water. Eventually, this lime was precipitated out on the bed of the sea, a process that was assisted by various living organisms that drew lime out of the water to form their shells.

And before leaving sedimentary rocks, it should be noted that the common iron ores — hematite and siderite — may occur as sedimentary beds.

Metamorphic rocks, the third and least common of the three main classifications, are igneous or sedimentary rocks that have suffered such physical and chemical changes through the forces of nature as to completely obscure their original identity. If subjected to, say, high temperatures and pressures, the original constituents might well be transformed into brand new minerals with the resulting mineral

Figure II-10 — An outcropping of gneiss, Lount Twp., Ontario.

particles readjusting themselves into parallel and flattened patterns. It is this laminated or banded feature that characterizes the metamorphic rocks, and makes their identification relatively simple. While at first glimpse this banding might suggest the sedimentary classification to the embryo geologist, a close examination will probably reveal the distinct crystal structure that marks the metamorphic rocks, rather than the cementing that features the sedimentary rocks.

Gneisses are a common group of metamorphic rocks (Fig. II-5). The term gneiss, when used alone, generally signifies a rock displaying the distinctive laminated feature of metamorphic rocks and one composed of quartz, feldspar and mica. A granite that is highly squeezed will result in the light and dark crystals being dragged into more or less long parallel bands. It is then termed a **granitic gneiss** (Fig. II-10). The word gneiss rhymes with "nice".

Another common and important group of metamorphic rocks, closely allied to the gneisses, are the **schists,** e.g. talc schist, mica schist, chlorite schist, etc. These prefixes are self explanatory, with the word schist implying a schistose or laminated structure, that is, one in which the recrystallized minerals have been oriented in parallel bands.

Figure II-11 — Varved clays deposited by the glacial Lake Kaministikiwa, south of Thunder Bay, Ontario. The banding results from the seasonal deposition, only fine silt being deposited in the winter months when ice covered the surface of the lake.

Figure II-12 — The ongoing geological process is demonstrated in this photo showing sand dunes near Heron Bay, Lake Superior, encroaching on the forest, some trees being already buried to considerable depth.

Shale, previously mentioned, when subjected to great pressure, is metamorphosed or changed into **slate,** once used in roofing as well as for the old fashioned schoolroom blackboard.

Quartzite is an extremely hard rock formed by the metamorphism of pure quartz sandstone.

Marble is another metamorphic rock, formed from limestone which has been recrystallized.

The next time you are taking a drive in the country, try and note the general formations in some of the rock cuts along the highways and see if you can classify them as to type. That is, if there is bedding, it will be apparent that it is sedimentary rock. Likewise, you should have little trouble in recognizing the parallel mineral banding of the gneisses, suggesting a metamorphic rock. On the other hand, if the rock appears to be massive, chances are that it is of igneous origin.

Turning from the rocks to the minerals, some thought should be given to their origin and mode of occurrence.

By far the greatest proportion of the minerals found in the earth's crust were formed during the solidification of molten materials or magmas. A lesser proportion was formed in the metamorphosis of older igneous and sedimentary rocks, through geologic processes involving heat and pressure. It should be pointed out that the interior of the earth is still very hot, and this is quite apparent in our deeper mine workings which do not really extend beyond relatively shallow depths into the crust.

Interior Rocks Very Hot

While there is a great variation the world over in the increase of rock temperature with depth, in the Precambrian Shield of Canada it is in the order of one degree Celsius for each 55 m to 110 m of depth. For example, at Kirkland Lake in Ontario, temperatures of 38°C were encountered at 2400 m below the surface, an increase of about 25°C in that depth.

In view of the temperature increases as noted above, it will be obvious that rocks hundreds of miles within the earth must be very hot. In addition to the heat, they are subjected to colossal pressures which keep them in a super-heated but solid state. But when any ruptures or weaknesses develop in the earth's crust, such as might be expected when it is folded into mountain ranges (the earth's surface is ever changing), the release of pressure will cause the super-heated rock to become fluid and spew out on surface, as lava from a volcano.

Cooling Process Important

Or, molten mass from the interior might force itself or intrude into any cracks or other points of weakness. These tongues of molten rock, which move out in many directions, may melt or alter the surrounding rock. Eventually, of course, the whole mass cools. It is this cooling which interests us most, for that is when the minerals, some of which are valuable, are formed.

Fortunately, most mineral constituents of molten lava crystallize at different temperatures,

and so tend to concentrate during the cooling process. It is these concentrations that often form our orebodies. But, there are many variations.

As each different mineral solidifies or crystallizes out of the melt, the composition of the melt will naturally change. So the end of this cooling process itself would find a concentration of some mineral. Or, in a process known to the geologist as **magmatic segregation,** the heavier minerals tend to sink in the semi-liquid mass and thus concentrate.

Some magmas are quite barren of valuable minerals, while others might contain such minerals as gold, silver, copper, lead, zinc, etc. The huge quantities of gases and liquids associated with igneous activity often contain valuable minerals and metals which are deposited as a result of reaction with other gases, liquids and solids. Other deposits may be formed by minerals dissolved in circulating waters and redeposited at some point where suitable chemical and physical conditions prevail. The natural processes of weathering may also be responsible for the concentration of minerals in economic quantities.

Inasmuch as no two orebodies are alike, comparison among mines is risky. Just because ore on a particular property, say, continues to depth, is no reason for assuming that ore on an adjoining property will follow the same trend. But this is getting into the economic aspects of the subject, which are touched on in the following chapter.

CHAPTER III

Economic Geology

Frequently, prospectors, would-be prospectors and mining speculators ask such questions as: "Where is a good place to look for a mine?", "Will such-and-such ever develop into a mine?", "Is that ore?", or, the commonest query of all, "Is it any good?" These questions, simple and direct as they are, are not always easily answerable. But on the other hand, the application of a few basic concepts of geology, coupled with the hard school of experience, may often prove helpful.

The old prospector's saw, "Gold is where you find it", isn't quite so, nor is his wishful theory that orebodies get richer with depth. While there is certainly an element of luck in the discovery of any orebody, locating one is usually more than just the result of fortuitous circumstances. The formation of an orebody calls for very special conditions.

But first, where should we look for a mine?

One of the most prolific mining areas in the world is the great Canadian Precambrian Shield which centers horseshoe-shaped around Hudson Bay and extends south to the Great Lakes, covering almost half the country (Figure III-1).

This shield is composed of our oldest known rocks, and includes the three general types discussed in the first chapter. Its geology is very complex. Fortunately, as the result of periods of mountain building, many favorable structural conditions have developed. Over the long eons of geological time, erosion has eaten away the mountains until all that remains are the spruce-covered hills that are seen today.

The Shield, which covers some 4,660,000 square kilometers, has, for the most part, been heavily glaciated. These glaciers, which consisted of great mountains of snow and ice, crept slowly southward in successive waves during comparatively recent geologic time. They constituted very strong forces, scouring the earth's surface and transporting much rock in the process.

Besides leaving prominent scratches or **striations** on the rock surfaces, the glaciers left numerous boulders as they melted and receded (Figure III-2), which were worn round by movement. These striations, by the way, run in a more or less north-south direction. As they show little deviation in any particular area, they can be helpful to a prospector or hunter who has lost his direction.

Flying over the relatively hummocky Shield country, the

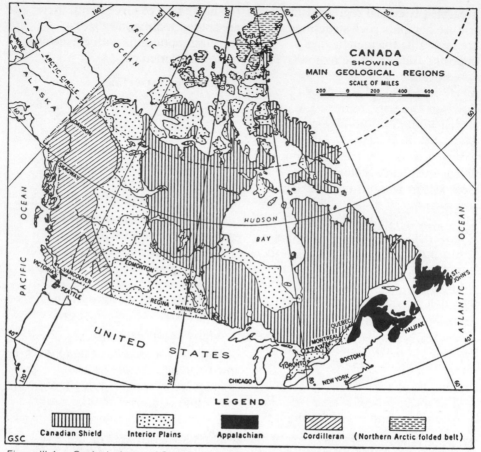

Figure III-1 — Geological map of Canada showing the five main geological regions.

observer is bound to be impressed by the myriad of lakes that dot its surface. He will also be comforted by their presence, for most of the conventional aircraft used in these areas are pontoon- or ski-equipped. In fact, there are few areas in the world that contain as many lakes as this one does.

Bordering the Precambrian Shield is another extensive area known as the Interior Plains. This includes a large portion of the Prairie Provinces. It is essentially an area of later sedimentary rocks which were laid down under great

lakes and seas that once covered the central part of the continent.

The rocks in this central region have not been subjected to any appreciable distortion. Consequently, there has been little igneous intrusion, so that these areas are for the most part unfavorable for the deposition of metalliferous deposits. But the region does contain large deposits of coal, oil and gas, as well as various types of industrial minerals, including gypsum, potash and other salt beds.

Both British Columbia and the Maritimes again each constitute separate geological regions. Both feature complex rock structures and are favorable for metallic ore deposits. Indeed, these regions contain some of the largest base metal deposits in the country — the Sullivan mine of Cominco Ltd., in British Columbia, and the copper-lead-zinc-silver deposits of both Brunswick Mining and Smelting Corp. and Heath Steele Mines, near Bathurst, N.B.

Although as yet it is only beginning to show an economic significance, there is a fifth geological region that embraces the Arctic Islands of Canada, some 1,295,000 square kilometers in extent. In recent years this region has been subjected to close geological study, with active exploration for oil and gas and metallic mineral deposits. It is interesting to note, for instance, that on Ellesmere Island, which lies to

the northwest of Greenland, there are folded sedimentary rocks forming mountains with elevations up to 3,650 meters.

Structure Important

It will be seen from the preceding, then, that mines are found over great areas of Canada. But how are we to find the most likely spots within these areas, since the search is not unlike looking for the proverbial needle in the haystack?

This is where structure comes into play for, besides the all-important requisite of an ample supply of ore-bearing solutions, it is necessary to have some type of opening into which the minerals can be deposited.

Many of our earlier mines outcropped on surface, and so were uncovered by the prospector's diligent search. But finding a mine isn't quite so simple these days, as

Figure III-2 — Greenstone, near Jackfish, Ontario, exhibiting a surface polished and scratched by glacial ice. The scratches are known as glacial striae.

most of the rock outcrops have been subjected to at least a cursory going over. So, various scientific methods have been devised to determine the geological conditions of the 90 per cent of the rock surface that is covered by overburden or water.

Gossans Hold Promise

But, let us not assume that all the orebodies that occur within the 10 per cent of the rocks that outcrop in this country have been found. A good example is that of Noranda's Geco mine, in the Manitouwadge area of Northwestern Ontario, found by the old fashioned pick and shovel method.

The clues that led to the initial Geco ore discovery were the words gossan and sulphides shown occurring within a greenstone belt on a government geological map that had been published some 20 years previously.

A **gossan** is simply the brown staining or rusty material overlying a mineral deposit, caused by the oxidation (decomposition) of a sulphide mineral, such as pyrite (iron sulphide).

What better clue than gossan would one want for finding copper, lead, zinc, etcetera, as such metals are almost invariably found associated with sulphides? In the case of Geco, the prospectors located the sulphides and gossan as shown on the map and noted that these occurred within a **shearing** or **break** which would provide a channel for ore solutions. They dug into the material for purposes of sampling. When the assay returns showed the presence of ore-making minerals, the ground was promptly

staked. It was sold shortly afterwards on terms that netted the alert prospectors several millions of dollars.

A gossan or rusty zone, therefore, is not without interest. However, inasmuch as the oxidation itself suggests that the minerals have been decomposed, it is important that trenches be dug into any rusty occurrence so that a fresh surface may be examined. This is a necessary precaution since any valuable minerals that may be present might have been leached out of the material on the surface.

Figure III-3 — Fault displacing bedded argillitic greywacke, Thunder Bay, Ontario. The displacement has dropped the right hand side about 3 m in relation to the left side.

Greenstone Belts Favored

At one time, prospectors and mining companies were inclined to confine their search for new mineral deposits to what are commonly referred to as **greenstone belts** — loosely defined as fine grained greenish rocks of igneous origin. In Canada's North, the term is generally restricted to highly altered lavas that were originally andesite, dacite or basalt.

Intrusions of igneous rocks into greenstone belts present favorable areas for prospecting, particularly in the vicinity of the **contact,** that is, the line along which the intrusive rock meets with the surrounding or intruded rock.

Some of these intrusions are of considerable magnitude, when they are known as **plugs** or **batholiths.** These extend to great depths, with the upper portions dome-like in shape (Fig. III-4). The contacts of these intrusions are seldom regular and clear cut. Rather, they are more likely to be jagged, with tongues protruding well into the older rocks. These latter, in turn, have sometimes been altered or changed by the hot intrusive rock.

Intrusive rocks may take the form of **dikes** or **sills.** The former are usually vein-like in appearance, having more or less parallel walls, often standing vertically, and, characteristically, are relatively narrow but long. Sills, on the other hand, are generally flat-lying intrusions that have great lateral extent compared to their thickness (Figure III-4, III-10).

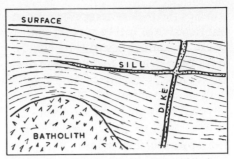

Figure III-4 — Sketch showing dome-shaped intrusive rock, known as a batholith extending from great depth. It may cover areal extent of many square miles. Other forms taken by intrusive rocks are known as dikes and sills.

On the subject of sills, it is interesting to note that at the Leitch gold mine, near Beardmore, Ont., the rich veins that persisted for 600 metres from surface were abruptly cut off at that horizon by a diabase rock formation. A study of this diabase revealed it to be a flat-lying sill of post-ore origin, about 180 metres thick. Inasmuch as it came in after the ore-bearing quartz veins, the company's geologists were confident that the veins would persist on the under side of the sill. A costly shaft program through the unproductive diabase was consequently undertaken. This was successful in developing the continuation of the same vein systems, and thus was added years to the profitable life of the mine. There are numerous examples in mining in which the downward extension of the ore structure is interrupted — and sometimes terminated — by an igneous intrusion.

Probably the most noted sill in Canadian mining is the gently-dipping diabase sill or sheet which underlies the Cobalt camp. Mostly, the silver veins were found on the upper side of the 300-meter-thick sill, but there were places where the undulating sill had bent upwards and been eroded away leaving exposed on the present surface silver veins which at one time lay underneath the sill. Veins on the upper side of the diabase continued downwards into the sill but only for a relatively short distance.

The most likely ground for ore deposition is deemed by many geologists and mining engineers to lie within a mile or so of contacts, rather than well within the intrusives themselves. Consequently, before prospecting crews are sent in to the field, the areas to be investigated are usually selected from a study of geological maps. A great deal of information can be gathered from a detailed study of these maps.

We have said that mineral bearing solutions are often introduced where rocks have been fractured, such as might be expected around bends or folds. Consequently, near the nose of a fold would be favorable hunting ground. These folds, again, are sometimes identified on the geological maps.

It will be seen, then, that the mine seeker places a great deal of dependence on geological maps. These are usually prepared from geological surveys which are being carried out continuously by the federal and provincial governments.

The mining industry, which is alert to the benefits to be derived from detailed geological mapping, keeps close tab on the release of any new geological map which can often signal a rush by interested prospectors and mining companies to acquire the most likely ground.

Figure III-5 — Drag folding in gneiss at Egan Chute, York River, Bancroft area, Ontario.

Figure III-6 — Differential erosion of diabase dike cutting granite on Highway 17, Montreal River, Northern Ontario.

Vein Deposits

Many of our ore deposits occur in veins or vein-type structures, so these are worthy of more than casual attention.

Although the earth's crust, to the layman, may seem to be a very solid mass, it actually contains many openings. Some are mere cracks, while others range to fissures that extend for considerable distances.

Circulating waters, which at great depths could exist only at very high temperatures and pressures (hence an excellent solvent), gradually find their way into fissures and ascend. As these mineral-laden waters rise, temperature and pressure gradually drop. When this takes place, the various mineral constituents held in solution begin to crystallize, and are deposited on the walls of the fissure.

Eventually the fissure becomes completely filled, forming a **vein.** The gold-bearing veins of the famous Porcupine and Kirkland Lake mines were formed in this fashion. They are, therefore, termed deep-seated deposits, which normally can be expected to persist to considerable depths.

Sometimes a small opening known to the geologist as a **vug** is left in the centre of a vein. These vugs are often lined with well formed mineral crystals, such as amethyst, a semi-precious stone commonly found within quartz veins.

Figure III-7 — Geologist examining rock sample.

Figure III-8 — A northern exploration camp. Rack for diamond drill core in left foreground.

Sulphides Important

Like the variations in the chemical composition of magmas, the chemical composition of the waters that form the vein occurrences also vary widely. Hence we get many different mineral associations in vein material. Sulphides, for instance, form an important group. The more common sulphides include **pyrite** (iron), **chalcopyrite** (copper), **sphalerite** (zinc) and **galena** (lead). Further mention of these minerals will be made later in this chapter.

In addition to the ore minerals just referred to, veins usually contain a much higher percentage of non-metallic mineral matter of little commercial use known as **gangue.** Quartz and calcite are the two commonest gangue minerals.

Frequently in granite country we get dikes known as **pegmatite.** A

pegmatite, in reality, has the same constituents as the granite itself. But, unlike ordinary dikes, the mineral composition of pegmatites is usually quite variable and inconsistent. The outstanding characteristic of these dikes are the large, coarse crystals of the various mineral constituents.

Specific mention is made of pegmatite occurrences because they frequently contain ore minerals. But, unfortunately, these are usually distributed so irregularly through the dike that they are often regarded as risky commercial propositions. Consequently, pegmatites require very careful sampling.

But pegmatite dikes, which are quite common, can be of commercial importance. In fact, they are frequently exploited for mica, feldspar and gemstones such as beryl and tourmaline. Less commonly, they are commercial sources of some of the rarer elements such as molybdenum, tin, lithium, a group known as the **rare earths** and a number of minerals of the radioactive family. The uranium mines of the Bancroft area, Southeastern Ontario, occur in pegmatites.

Secondary Enrichment

Before leaving the subject of veins, when considering their economic aspects, the matter of secondary enrichment, a process which might be described as natural salting, deserves comment.

As the surface of the earth is worn by erosion, the uppermost portion of the vein (or other type of ore deposit) is gradually worn away. But some of the metallic content of the eroded portion may be carried down into the vein by descending oxidizing waters and re-deposited at a deeper horizon, resulting in what is known as **secondary enrichment.** It is nature's process of making high grade out of low grade ores.

In most parts of the Precambrian Shield, which has been heavily glaciated, secondary enrichment is not usually a serious factor. Nevertheless, a careful and conscientious prospector sampling a new discovery will be careful to dig down to a fresh surface before cutting his sample.

In countries that have not been glaciated, secondary enrichment can be very important, for the mineral content of an orebody might decrease very quickly as soon as workings are carried below this zone of enrichment. But, in some cases, this carries to surprising depths.

Figure III-9 — Rock trench cut across surface outcrop.

Figure III-10 — Red Rock cuesta on Highway 17, Northern Ontario, a 'hogback' formed because the harder diabase sill is more resistant to erosion than the underlying sediments.

Gold in Quartz Veins

Gold is usually found in quartz veins, but is also found in replacement bodies, in which case it is frequently associated with copper and zinc.

In veins, it normally occurs in the native state, since gold combines chemically with few other elements. It does, however, tend to be intimately associated with sulphides such as pyrite, arsenopyrite and chalcopyrite, which are described subsequently.

The association of gold with sulphides may form what is termed as **refractory ore,** which spells milling and metallurgical complications. These are usually solved by roasting the sulphides after they are concentrated in the mill.

Most readers have seen gold and are more or less familiar with its distinctive and beautiful yellow color. Oddly enough, though, the miner working in even the richest gold mines seldom sees the metal in the ore he is extracting. Its occurrence is frequently microscopic in size. It is the exception, not the rule, to see gold with the naked eye in most ores. Very rarely, it is found in extremely rich concentrations, these being museum specimens. The bulk of our gold production comes from medium to low grade ores and as byproducts of base metal mines.

Silver With Gold

Gold usually carries some silver with it. Deep-seated deposits such as are found in the Precambrian Shield (Kirkland Lake and Porcupine, for example), have only a minor amount of silver, but in gold deposits formed at shallower depths, the percentage of the white metal may be quite high. Examples of this are to be found in a number of British Columbia occurrences. A high silver-to-gold ratio, then, suggests a shallow deposit.

Principal Canadian production of silver is derived as a byproduct from base metal mining, it being usually associated with galena.

Galena, the principal sulphide of lead, occurs in both vein and replacement deposits. It has a high metallic lustre, is lead-gray in color, and generally forms in cubic crystals which can be readily seen with the naked eye. Galena is a very heavy mineral, and is soft enough to be easily scratched with a knife blade.

Outstanding examples of silver-bearing galena are to be found at the Sullivan mine of Cominco Ltd. in British Columbia and at United Keno Hill Mines in the Yukon. Canada's leading silver producer is now the Kidd Creek mine of Texasgulf Inc., where the silver is found associated with galena.

But silver also occurs in important concentrations in the native or free state, as in the calcite veins of Ontario's Cobalt and Gowganda districts. These veins likewise carry **argentite,** a sulphide of the white metal that is a dark lead-gray in color but usually tarnished to a dull black.

Copper

Copper occurs most commonly as **chalcopyrite,** a sulphide of copper and iron. Chalcopyrite is brass-yellow to golden in color, but is frequently tarnished to show brilliant iridescent hues. In quartz veins it is sometimes confused with gold, but is brittle. It may be confused, too, with pyrite, but the color is slightly more yellow. And it can be scratched more readily than pyrite.

Chalcopyrite is by far the most important ore of copper, commonly found in deposits associated with other sulphides or disseminated through igneous rocks. It also occurs as replacements and in what are

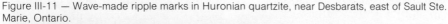

Figure III-11 — Wave-made ripple marks in Huronian quartzite, near Desbarats, east of Sault Ste. Marie, Ontario.

Figure III-12 — Left: Prospector squares claim post before writing particulars of number, date, etc. Right: Panning for gold is pretty much a lost art but the gold pan is still a useful tool as a rough method of determining content of heavy metals.

known as contact metamorphic deposits.

Incidentally, an analysis of pure chalcopyrite would show 34.5% copper, 35% sulphur and 30.5% iron. Therefore, theoretically, the highest copper content possible in chalcopyrite ore would be 34.5%. Such a content never occurs in nature. A 10% copper ore would be considered very high grade. At the Lornex mine in British Columbia, for instance, the copper content is less than 0.5% which is equivalent to only 10 lb. per ton, or 5.0 kg per tonne.

But copper, too, is occasionally found in the native state, one location being around the south shore of Lake Superior where it occurs as **amygdaloids.** These are bubble holes in lava, caused by escaping gases, which have been subsequently filled by minerals.

Copper Seldom Alone

Gold, silver and zinc are often found with copper sulphide deposits.

Lead and zinc, which are frequently closely associated, occur most commonly as their respective sulphides, **galena** and **sphalerite.** Again, these important ore minerals may be found in veins, as replacement deposits or as disseminations, such as in the extensive lead-zinc deposits at Pine Point Mines on the south shore of Great Slave Lake in the Northwest Territories.

Sphalerite is perhaps the most difficult of the common sulphides to identify, inasmuch as its color varies widely. However, it is most commonly yellow, brown, or black, and is characterized by its resinous lustre, and usually exhibits a rather distinct cleavage, which means its structure is such that it will persistently break in the same direction.

Canada is the largest supplier of nickel to the Free World and accounts for about two-thirds of the total supply. This is provided by two provinces, Ontario and Manitoba. Nearly 60% of the Canadian capacity comes from the Sudbury area of Ontario. The nickel there is extracted from the sulphide mineral **pentlandite,** which in turn is characteristically intimately associated with the more common iron sulphide, **pyrrhotite.** The latter is usually a reddish bronze in color, and can be readily distinguished from the other common sulphides already discussed because of the fact that it is magnetic and will attract a compass needle.

While pyrrhotite is, in reality, mined for its associated nickel, the iron content is also being economically recovered as a byproduct in the Sudbury area. These Sudbury deposits also yield appreciable amounts of copper (Inco Limited is Canada's biggest producer of copper), the platinum-group metals, gold and silver.

"Fool's Gold"

Left to the last is perhaps the most common sulphide of all, **pyrite.** This, to the prospector, is "fool's gold". It is pale, brass-yellow in color, being nearly uniform. It is most likely to be confused with chalcopyrite, but it is both harder and paler in color than the latter, and frequently forms in cubic crystals.

Pyrite often carries small amounts of copper and gold, so can be considered an important ore of these metals. It is an iron sulphide, and in certain circumstances can be mined for both its sulphur and iron content. Processes have been developed to recover the iron and sulphur contained in pyrite but so far they have not proven economic in Canada.

Pure pyrite contains 47% iron and 53% sulphur.

Iron Ores

Turning from the non-ferrous minerals, the largest commercial iron deposits occur as **hematite,** a mineral that may be formed in various ways and which is found in rocks of all ages. Its color ranges from red to dark gray, but regardless of its color, it has a characteristic red **streak.** (Streak is simply the color of the mineral powder and is best seen by scratching the mineral on an unglazed bathroom tile.)

Hematite is very heavy and non-magnetic. When pure, it contains 70% iron. The iron ore deposits of the Steep Rock range in Northwestern Ontario are composed of hematite. Large deposits are mined in Australia and elsewhere around the world.

Magnetite Important

Another important ore mineral of iron is **magnetite,** which is a black, heavy oxide with a metallic lustre. Its most distinguishing characteristic is its magnetism. When pure, it contains 72.4% iron. It is found in veins, contact metamorphic or replacement deposits. Magnetite is mined at Quebec Cartier in Quebec, along the Labrador Trough, and in various small deposits in British Columbia. It is a principal ore in Sweden.

Magnetite, too, is a widespread accessory mineral forming small grains in many igneous rocks. When these rocks weather, the magnetite often concentrates into black beach sands. These black bands may be seen near the water's edge on almost any beach on lakes within the Precambrian Shield.

A cherty on jaspery rock found in the Lake Superior ranges is known as **taconite.** It is a bedded, extremely hard iron formation, including disseminated hematite and magnetite, which has developed as an important source of low grade iron ore.

In the Michipicoten district of Ontario, Algoma Steel Corporation is profitably mining extensive deposits of an iron carbonate mineral known as **siderite.** This is light brown in color, having what is termed a vitreous to pearly lustre, and can be readily scratched with a knife blade.

Before being used as an iron ore, siderite requires beneficiation by roasting to drive off the carbon dioxide content of the mineral, thus raising its iron content to a point suitable for the blast furnace.

Uranium Minerals

Since the development of atomic energy following World War II, uranium has become one of the most sought metals in the world, as it is so far the only naturally occurring substance used as a basic raw material in the production of nuclear energy. The more plentiful thorium has not yet reached its potential in this regard.

Uranium never occurs in its pure form in nature. Rather, it is combined with other substances to form over a hundred known uranium-bearing minerals.

In Canada, one of the leading uranium producers of the world, uranium is found in **primary mineral deposits,** that is, those that have not been changed since they were originally deposited.

Pitchblende is by far the most important uranium mineral, being the chief constitutent of most uranium ores. It is essentially uranium oxide, frequently occurring in vein deposits as at the Eldorado mine at Great Bear Lake, Northwest Territories, and in the Beaverlodge area, Saskatchewan. It does not form in crystals. When massive, it breaks with a curved surface as does glass. Dark grayish-black in color, it is heavier than iron and hard as steel. Exceptionally rich deposits have been found at several locations in Saskatchewan. At Elliot Lake, in Ontario, the grade is much lower but the tonnages are large. Here the radioactive mineral is finely disseminated and not easily identified.

Uranium Frequently Shows Stain

Another important primary uranium mineral is **uraninite,** which has the same color as well as most of the other properties, and characteristics of pitchblende, except that it occurs in the form of small cube-shaped crystals rather than as rounded or irregular masses. It is usually found in pegmatite dikes.

All uranium-bearing minerals emit radioactive rays, which may be detected with a geiger or scintillation counter.

Prospectors searching for uranium keep a sharp eye for the presence of a bright yellow or orange crust or powder surrounding any dark mineral, as this is a distinctive indication of the presence of this mineral. In fact, any yellow, green or orange coloring along cracks or joints in rocks should be carefully investigated.

Ores of Metals and Industrial Minerals

Metal or Mineral	Chemical Symbol	Common Ore Mineral
Aluminum	Al	Bauxite (hydrated aluminum oxide)
Asbestos		Chrysotile (hydrous magnesium silicate)
Barite		Barite (barium sulphate)
Cobalt	Co	Cobaltite (cobalt sulpharsenide, 35.5% Co) Smaltite (cobalt, nickel, iron triarsenide, 21% Co)
Columbium	Cb	Now called Niobium
Chromium	Cr	Chromite (ferrous chromic oxide)
Copper	Cu	Native copper Chalcopyrite (copper iron sulphide, 34.5% Cu) Chalcocite (copper sulphide, 79.8% Cu)
Gold	Au	Native gold
Gypsum		Gypsum (hydrous calcium sulphate)
Iron	Fe	Hematite (iron oxide, 70% Fe) Magnetite (iron oxide, 72.4% Fe) Siderite (iron carbonate, 48% Fe)
Lead	Pb	Galena (lead sulphide, 86.6% Pb)
Magnesium	Mg	Dolomite (calcium magnesium carbonate) Magnesite (magnesium carbonate)
Manganese	Mn	Pyrolusite (manganese dioxide, 63.2% Mn)

Metal or Mineral	Chemical Symbol	Common Ore Mineral
Mercury	Hg	Cinnabar (mercury sulphide, 86.2% Hg)
Mica		Muscovite (potassium aluminum silicate) Biotite (potassium, magnesium, iron aluminum silicate)
Molybdenum	Mo	Molybdenite (molybdenum disulphide, 60% Mo)
Nickel	Ni	Pentlandite (nickel iron sulphide, 22% Ni) Niccolite (nickel arsenide, 43.9% Ni)
Niobium	Nb	Columbite (iron manganese niobate, 77% Nb_2O_5) Pyrochlore (complex oxide of varied composition)
Potash	K_2O	Sylvanite (potasium chloride, 63.2% K_2O equivalent)
Salt	NaCl	Halite (sodium chloride)
Silver	Ag	Native silver Argentite (silver sulphide, 87.1% Ag)
Tin	Sn	Cassiterite (tin oxide, 78.6% Sn)
Titanium	Ti	Ilmenite (iron titanium oxide, 31.6% Ti)
Tungsten	W	Scheelite (calcium tungstate, 80.5% WO_3) Wolframite (iron manganese tungstate, 76.5% WO_3)
Uranium	U	Uraninite (uranium oxide, 50-85% U_3O_8) Pitchblende (uranium oxide, 50-58% U_3O_8)
Zinc	Zn	Sphalerite (zinc sulphide, 67% Zn)

N.B.: The percentages shown are the theoretical content of the metal or metallic oxide contained in the pure mineral.

Claim Staking

The first concern of a successful searcher is to have reserved for himself the benefits that can accrue through his effort and powers of observation and deduction. He is enabled to do this by the power of the laws which govern and regulate the mineral affairs in the particular jurisdiction concerned. This principle is common to all businesses, and a reasonable knowledge of the pertinent law is essential in all areas of commerce.

In most countries, it would appear that the supervision of natural resources is vested in the secondary level of government, as in the Provinces in Canada, the States in the United States, and so forth. In general, the intent and spirit of the legislation is directed toward: (i) securing to bona fide persons and companies the exclusive right to pursue development of a discovery, (ii) the protection of the public interest, (iii) the actual encouragement of sub-surface exploration through various devices of legislation, and (iv) providing the means whereby disputes may be settled quickly and at minimum expense. Our outline example in claim staking is taken from the Mining Act of Ontario, though the would-be prospector is cautioned that in another jurisdiction he should avail himself of the local legislation, and study it thoroughly.

A person who sets out to stake claims must first obtain a Miner's Licence which is available to all persons age 18 and over, and to companies, on application and payment of the appropriate fees.

A mining claim in Ontario is a square plot of land, measuring about 400 meters (1,320 ft.) on a side, with its boundaries oriented in north-south and east-west directions, and containing an area of about 16 hectares (40 acres). The boundaries are denoted by four posts, of which the first, or No. 1, is placed at the northeast corner, and so on clockwise round the claim to No. 4 at the northwest corner. The claim lines are also indicated by blazing the trees at intervals or, if the area is treeless, by the setting of suitable pickets. On the No. 1 post at the northeast corner, the stake must be marked with the staker's name, the number of his licence, the date, and the time staked (Fig. III-12). The other three posts must be marked with his name and licence number.

If a corner of a claim is inaccessible, owing for instance, to its being in a lake, a **witness post** is set on the claim line, and this post must indicate the direction and distance to that post to which it is a witness.

Within thirty-one days, the staker must apply for a recording of the claim, or claims, at the office of the Mining Recorder in the mining district concerned, provide certain prescribed information which will identify the location of the claim or claims, and pay a modest fee in respect of each claim staked. He is then issued a set of metal tags (if he has not provided himself with same before setting out to stake), and these must be affixed to the corner posts within six months. Then, the claim is considered to be properly staked.

At this point, the staker is possessor of an exclusive right to proceed with the exploration and development of his claim, or group of claims, and this can be defended against all comers provided that he does all that the rules prescribe. To keep his rights alive, this includes a requirement that he perform work on his claims totalling 200 man-days per claim over five years, beginning with 40 days in the first year. Such work is known as **assessment work,** must be reported and sworn to before the Mining Recorder, and is also subject to check. Failure to perform the work is considered to mean that he wishes to abandon his rights in the claim, or claims, in which case it falls open for staking by someone else. On completion of the five years of assessment work, a survey of the claim, and the payment of all taxes required, he may obtain a twenty-one year lease. After the property has been in production on a substantial scale and continuously for at least one year, the leaseholder may apply for a patent respecting the lands or rights held under the lease.

Assessment work may take many forms, and by doing certain kinds such as diamond drilling, geophysical prospecting, and other activity designed to obtain knowledge of sub-surface conditions, he is in effect allowed to multiply the man-hours actually expended, by certain factors which are specified in the rules.

In many cases terrain is covered by overburden to depths and extents that preclude prospecting by other than geophysical or other highly technical methods. In such instances, under the Ontario Mining Act for example, a concession licence may be applied for, and its issuance grants the licensee exclusive right to prospect the designated area, which must not exceed 26,000 hectares in area, for a term of three years. The fees for such a concession, and the general rules regarding work requirements, are such as to compel a high level of diligence and expertise in efforts to prospect the ground covered. If a deposit of mineral becomes authentically revealed in this work, the licensee may apply for and obtain a ten-year lease on an area comprising not more than one-tenth of the concession area.

These few paragraphs contain only the salient points in the legislation dealing with the acquisition and holding of mineral lands. The actual legislation is much more complex, but in every detail it is prompted by the spirit outlined in the second paragraph under this heading. Further information may be obtained from the legislation itself, as it may concern the jurisdiction in which the reader may be interested.

CHAPTER IV

Scientific Prospecting

It has been truly said that "an orebody is an accident in the earth's crust."

Until relatively recent years, mineral exploration in Canada and elsewhere has followed along fairly straight surface geological reconnaissance. This process begins with highly trained geologists who examine the country and note all of the geological features as revealed in outcrops and other natural exposures. The geological reports and maps resulting from this activity form a principal part of the equipment of experienced prospectors, who examine in closer detail the more favorable areas indicated.

In all cases, and this extends to the so-called modern methods, what is sought is a geological condition which is different from its surroundings in some peculiar way. It may be a structure, an abrupt change in rock types, a contact, a sign of chemical alteration, or whatever else may characterize the possible presence of an ancient accident which may just possibly turn out to have been accompanied by ore deposition.

It has already been pointed out that our surface outcrops have been subject to at least a cursory examination. It follows from this that it is highly probable that those orebodies which outcrop on surface have already been found. For future mineral discovery we must be able to extract information from structures overlain by heavy overburden, or by rock capping. For some time now we have had a growing body of a special kind of knowledge at work in these situations, and which we refer to as geophysics.

Properly, **geophysics** is the study of the physical properties of the earth. As its name suggests, it combines the deductive science of geology with the more precise science of physics. Its practitioners are **geophysicists,** and they work in close association with geologists and mining engineers in the purpose of making mineral exploration more fruitful and economic. The effort of this teamwork has proven very successful. Geophysics will not often by itself, no more than will conventional geology by itself, definitely identify a buried orebody, but it provides, like other exploration methods, clues in the search for mineral concentrations.

If we allow the activities of seventeenth century Swedish prospectors, who used magnetized iron bars to assist in the finding of magnetic bodies of iron ore,

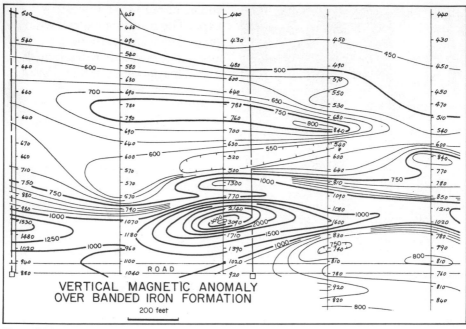

VERTICAL MAGNETIC ANOMALY
OVER BANDED IRON FORMATION

200 feet

Figure IV-1 — An anomaly revealed by a magnetometer survey with contour lines drawn through points of equal magnetic intensity, as measured by the vertical component.

geophysics is not a new science. Its development is related with progress in physics and geology, particularly advances in electronics and in the understanding of the physical properties of mineral deposits and their environment. In recent years, with the advent of magnetic recording, computers, and mini processors, the amount of data we can acquire and process has increased spectacularly.

Among other things, the earth is a large magnet, with lines of magnetic force wandering very roughly along the meridians. The rocks composing its crust vary in many ways, in physical properties as well as in chemical composition. These include: electrical conductivity, degrees of elasticity and other properties of rocks which determine wave propagation through them, relative specific gravity,

radioactivity, and the ways in which they respond to artificial electromagnetic fields. The methods used to measure the various properties are not, however, in competition, for they are frequently used to complement each other.

In all geophysical surveys, what is actually sought is an **anomaly** in the true sense as the Oxford dictionary puts it, 'irregularity, deviation from the common or natural order; exceptional condition or circumstance.' A simple, though excellent anomaly is shown in Figure IV-1 which concerns a part of a magnetic survey. In that survey, the magnetic field has been measured at short intervals over an area, and the values found at various grid positions plotted on a plan. Lines were drawn through points having equal value, in a manner corresponding exactly with the isobars of our familiar weather maps. The resulting pattern which is roughly concentric, shows an anomalous magnetic behaviour. It is important to point out that that is all it does show, though it is just possible that it is caused by the presence of an orebody. It does, however, arouse interest, depending upon the magnitude of the phenomena being investigated, and other means may be pursued to centre upon the cause of the disturbance.

Another kind of picture, or set of pictures, could also have been produced from the same data by drawing profiles of the phenomena along various section lines. These are commonly used by geophysicists and geologists together as guides to determine the means of further investigation.

Magnetic Methods

The longest known physical feature of the earth is its magnetism. At any point on the earth's surface the local magnetic field is made up of lines of force which can be expressed in terms of strength, direction, and inclination. A mass of rock with a high magnetic susceptibility will attract lines of force to itself, causing a distortion relative to the surrounding area with respect to direction and inclination, and to intensity of field strength. The simplest instruments for magnetic prospecting are the compass and dip needle for direction and inclination of the field. Magnetic field strengths are measured with fluxgate or proton precession magnetometers (Figure IV-2), which commonly measure these in terms of vertical and total field, respectively. An idea

Figure IV-2 — MF-2-100 Analogue Fluxgate Magnetometer for measuring vertical component of earth's magnetic field.

Figure IV-3 — Helicopter electromagnetic systems such as the HEM-802 are used in base metal exploration in mountainous terrain.

of their sensitivity is given by the unit in which they measure. This unit is the **gamma** which is but one one-hundred-thousandth part of the **gauss** which the reader may remember from high school physics.

All three of the types of instruments suggested here are used to search for bodies of higher magnetic susceptibility, such as may be represented in deposits of magnetite, as the most obvious example, as well as of certain sulphides of iron. Unfortunately, many worthless basic intrusives also show good values of magnetic susceptibility, and small differences are usually present as we pass from one rock type to another. This property is used in many ways, even toward the delineation of structures which may possibly include oil traps.

Of particular interest is the aerial magnetometer, an extremely sensitive instrument which is trailed below an aeroplane or a helicopter, or mounted on the aircraft in a so-called stinger (Figures IV-3, IV-7). By combining readings from this instrument with continuous aerial photography, the character of the magnetic field of a large area can be plotted. If an important anomaly is revealed in such work, more detailed surveys are carried out on the ground. Our governments have done a great deal of aeromagnetic surveying over recent years, and the resulting maps have led to important mineral discoveries in Ontario and elsewhere. The magnetic iron deposit at Marmora in eastern Ontario was first indicated in such a survey, and it is overlain by some hundred feet of barren limestone capping.

There are several electrical and electromagnetic methods used in geophysics, and we shall begin with that which is referred to as the **self-potential,** not because it is widely used itself, but because it led to one of the most useful electrical methods yet developed.

A sulphide body extending above and below a water table will be attacked by the oxygen contained in the surface waters, with the generation of minute quantities of sulphuric acid. In turn, this will be neutralized by various components in the surrounding rocks, particularly by carbonates, to form various mild salts. These will be in equilibrium with the pyrite at a different electric potential from the solution which is in contact with the sulphides below the water table. This causes a current to pass through the rocks from the lower, or "positive" end to the upper "negative" end. In other words, the sulphide body acts as a weak electric battery. The currents are often measurable in terms of **milliamperes,** though unfortunately the manifestation will be the same, whether the cause is a body of valuable copper ore, or merely a body of low grade pyrite or pyrrhotite. The technique is not widely used, however, and has not produced any economic result.

Figure IV-4 — Portable TSQ-2 transmitters can be used for induced polarization, resistivity or electromagnetic measurements.

Induced Polarization

It has, however, given rise to another electrical method which is now in wide use and is known as the **induced polarization** technique, actually discovered in the 1920s but refined in more recent years. In its simplest terms, it relates to the well known phenomena of a flashlight bulb energized by an old battery; as we know, when the switch is turned on the bulb will glow briefly, and then weaken. In other words, electric energy is polarized near the terminals of the battery. When an alternating current is artificially pressed into a sulphide orebody, something like that takes place, and the method is concerned with detecting the electric surface polarization of metallic minerals, and which is induced by the electrical currents applied to the ground. The forces which oppose the current flow are said to polarize the interfaces between metallic minerals and solutions in pore

Figure IV-5 — The Pulse EM system which can be used for surveying drill holes to depths of 300 meters, or more. It will detect conductive sulphides up to 100 metres from the side of the hole.

passages, and an overvoltage has to be applied to drive the current across these barriers. When the inducing current is switched off, the overvoltage decays, but only with time. In other words, there is a brief storage of energy whose dissipation is measurable after the current is switched off. As a technique, induced polarization is very useful in the economic layout of exploration drilling of sulphide orebodies (Figures IV-4, IV-5).

In **resistivity** methods, an artificial electric current is pressed into the ground of an area being explored, and the behaviour of the electrical field studied by probing the ground with pairs of electrodes connected to very sensitive milliammeters. The resistances offered by the various rocks are carefully measured in terms of ohm-centimeters, and anomalies noted from their plot on a plan. An orebody containing metallic sulphides will cause an anomalously low resistance. So, however, will a fault plane lined with worthless graphitic material, a barren sulphide, or a water course containing a brackish solution.

The most important of the methods now in general use, particularly from the standpoint of economic result, are the so-called **electromagnetic (EM)** methods. If an alternating current is pressed into a loop of wire held above the surface of the earth, a current will be induced to flow in any buried conductive deposit below it. The phenonmenon is similar to what takes place in the familiar A-C

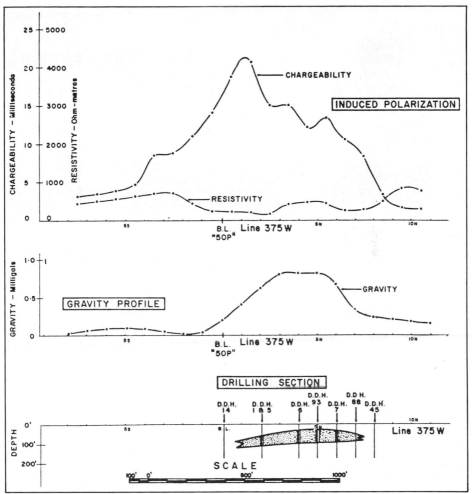

Figure IV-6 — Geophysical profiles over the Pyramid No. 1 orebody, Pine Point, N.W.T. From a paper by H. O. Seigel, H. L. Hill and J. G. Baird, published in "Geophysics", August, 1968.

induction motor, in that an alternating magnetic field is formed, and this induces a secondary alternating current to flow through the sub-surface conductor. This induced current creates its own alternating magnetic field, which is measured by a search coil connected to a sensitive voltmeter, or through an amplifier and thence to a pair of earphones. The actual measurements taken will include the actual millivoltage of the induced current, and often, the phase difference between the applied and the induced currents. As with all geophysical methods, the technique involves the detection of anomalies in the transmitted electromagnetic field. Such anomalies may be caused by bodies other than base metal sulphides, however, and careful interpretation of the results is necessary to single out suitable targets for drilling.

A number of different EM methods, each with its own

Figure IV-7 — The Tridem airborne electromagnetic system can be flown in conjunction with VLF, magnetometer and radiometric instrumentation for complete one-pass geophysical surveying.

particular capabilities and limitations, is used by the industry. Airborne versions have become very important in the early phases of exploration (Fig. IV-7)

Electromagnetic methods have made an important contribution to a number of economic discoveries.

Gravity Methods

The gravitational force of attraction of any body toward the earth is very well known. Actually, this is a universal phenomenon, and there is a mutual gravitational attraction between any two bodies in direct proportion to the product of their masses. Thus, a body which is moved from place to place will actually weigh more over a dense rock material than it will over a light mass, as say a dome of salt. The basic unit of gravitational force is the **gal,** and the average gravitational attraction at the face of the earth is about 980 gals. In geophysical work, however, much finer measurements than this indicates may be important, and the geophysicist uses a unit known as the **milligal,** or one thousandth of a gal. This suggests an extraordinary

Figure IV-8 — Gravity meters such as the Scintrex CG-2 make measurements of the earth's gravity field with a sensitivity of one part per million.

sensitivity in instrumentation, and such is the case in the gravity meters used in present-day geophysics.

In application, anomalies are sought which indicate differences in rock types in terms of their relative densities. Gravity methods are most widely used in petroleum exploration, though their use is extending into other fields as well. For instance, whether an anomaly is caused by a sulphide body or by a

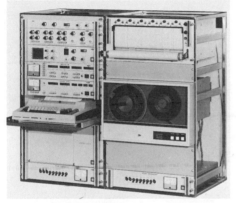

Figure IV-9 — The Spectra II records gamma rays over the whole radioactive spectrum and differentiates between potassium, thorium and uranium. Used in uranium exploration, it can be installed in helicopter or fixed wing aircraft.

graphitic shear can often be clarified by a gravity survey. Another way in which gravity surveys can be useful is in the rapid reconnaissance of an area in attempts to delineate sub-regions as between major rock types, and thus help to indicate ground favorable to exploration by other methods.

For hundreds of years mankind has had instruments for the measurement of amplitude, and the direction of, earthquake shocks. The propagation of these shocks is partly a function of the elastic properties of the rocks through which they are transmitted. It has been recognized for many years that different geological formations will exert different effects upon the speed at which earthquake shocks travel.

While seismic prospecting techniques are pretty well confined to petroleum exploration, where they are an important tool, there may one day emerge situations in mineral exploration in which they may be of use. In practice, a small earthquake is generated at a selected point by firing a charge of explosives in a shallow drill hole, and measuring the propagation speed of the shock waves as they pass through the strata of the formation under investigation. An important phenomenon is the reflecting effect at various interfaces between the various strata. By tracing the depths of these interfaces, important structural information is obtained and may lead to the location of structures favorable to the collection of petroleum.

Radiometric Surveys

The now familiar **Geiger counter** gives an indirect indication of the presence of radioactive substances by measuring some of the products of their decay. In the decay of uranium, for instance, three kinds of rays are given off, **alpha, beta,** and **gamma.** Of these, the gamma is the most penetrating, and thus the most likely to be detected by the Geiger counter. The Geiger has a low operating efficiency and sensitivity, and in many applications has been supplanted by an instrument known as a **scintillation counter.**

The scintillation counter operates upon a different principle from that of the Geiger, and the impulses generated in its detecting unit can be magnified many times. The instrument can be made selective for the detection of either gamma or alpha rays, and in any case is much more sensitive. It has also been adapted for use in aerial surveys.

Figure IV-10 — A portable gamma ray spectrometer capable of simultaneous measurements of potassium, uranium, thorium and total energy. Used for uranium prospecting, geologic mapping, and ground follow-up of airborne radiometric surveys.

Gamma-ray spectrometers are even more advanced scintillation counters, which distinguish between radiation from the three main radioactive elements, uranium, potassium and thorium.

Radon surveys are becoming increasingly common in the search for uranium. One of the radioactive decay products or uranium, radon gas can diffuse or be transported some distance through fissures and unconsolidated material and thus serve to indicate the presence of buried uranium.

To measure the concentration of radon isotopes within the gases contained in soils and sub-soils, an emanometer or radon monor monitor is used. New developments are **Alpha Meter** and **Track Etch** methods in which the alpha radiation from radon is recorded on film or electronically counted by small devices that are placed in holes 2 ft. (75 cm) deep in a grid pattern over the area being explored. After being left undisturbed for a certain length of time these devices are retrieved and the counts recorded or the film processed.

As well as in prospecting for radioactive minerals, members of the scintillation counter family are widely used in the logging of oil wells in areas where the more favorable strata are known or suspected to have minute disseminations of radioactive substances. It should be pointed out that all work in fields of radioactive phenomena is subject to many interfering factors.

Geochemical Methods

Exploration geochemistry is based on the fact that mineral deposits constitute an "anomalous" concentration of one or more metals on the earth's crust, thus contrasting strongly with the surrounding background country rock. During the process of surface and near surface weathering these anomalous concentrations of metals become incorporated in near surface weathering products such as stream and lake sediments, ground and surface waters, soils and vegetation by the natural processes of chemical and mechanical movement. This movement spreads the anomalous concentrations outwards from the

Figure IV 11 — Collecting a sample of sediment from a stream.

source giving a dispersion halo which provides a considerably larger exploration target than the deposit itself.

During an exploration program, samples may be collected from rocks, soils, sediments, water, and vegetation as appropriate and typically are analysed for the ore-forming elements and in certain cases, also for associated pathfinder elements.

Geochemistry is now used on a routine basis in most exploration programs. In temperate areas with residual soil, it is frequently the most important exploration technique while in some glaciated areas, where the use of geochemistry may be more complex depending on the exact nature of the glacial history of the area, its use may be relatively minor.

More Than One Used

The selection of the most suitable geophysical method for use in a particular area will depend upon a number of considerations, such as the expected physical properties of the mineralization looked for and of its environment, topography, climate, availability of equipment, etcetera. Usually, several different methods will have to be used simultaneously, or in a certain sequence, for the geophysical exploration phase to be more effective.

In any case, geophysical investigation has proven economically useful toward the economic planning of the next step in the exploration program, the one which gives the first real "proof of the pudding". This is diamond drilling which is the subject of the next chapter.

In this chapter we have outlined, at the risk of oversimplification, the most prominent science-based methods that are used in present day mineral exploration. It is not to say, however, that the prospector who has been of first importance in the mineral history of Canada and elsewhere, has passed from the picture. His role, of course, is undergoing modification, but lightweight geophysical prospecting tools are making his task less arduous and more efficient.

It is also hoped that there has been dispelled any notion that there is any royal road to mineral discovery, and most particularly in these days when most of, if not all, of the mineral deposits outcropping on surface have already been discovered. Future discoveries will only be the result of the bringing together human resources which embrace special degrees of expertise, and the older requirements of fortitude and financial courage remain as operative as they were in years gone by.

CHAPTER V

Probing Beneath the Surface

The diamond core drill has probably found more extensive use in Canada than in any country in the world. Canadian diamond drilling crews are noted for their skill, energy and experience and are in demand in every corner of the globe.

Diamond drilling has always been a very necessary part of the mining business and as the business world grows more complex, there has been a parallel need in mining to prove greater ore reserves to substantiate the huge financial commitments needed for new mines or for plant additions for existing ones.

The primary function of the diamond drill is to secure a core of the earth's crust. Through thorough analysis of this rock core, the presence of mineralized zones can be revealed and their market value determined.

The whole history of mining is replete with stories of discoveries made and proven with diamond drill holes. In years past, the venturesome prospector made a tremendous contribution to the development of Canada by discoveries made through his examination of surface outcrops across this land. The social and economic development of cities and towns like Kimberley, Uranium City, Thompson, Flin Flon, Timmins, Red Lake,

Manitouwadge, Sudbury, Elliot Lake, Noranda, Val d'Or, and Chibougamau to name but a few, are testimony to his contributions.

Probably most, if not all, of the surface discoveries have been made, and for the most part, the prospector has been replaced by sophisticated exploration teams involving expert geological reconnaissance and the use of aerial and ground geophysical surveys. The latter can reveal anomalous conditions within the earth that are masked from view by unconsolidated ground cover or waste rock material. The anomalies may, or may not, contain minerals worthy of development and must be probed by the diamond drill to determine if valuable metals are present.

As with other industries, diamond drilling has advanced appreciably in recent years. This applies to both the technique and the equipment itself. Indications of diamond drilling can be found as far back in history as the early Egyptians who made use of it in the construction of the pyramids. With the introduction of steam power in the late 1800s, use of the diamond drill expanded rapidly and spread to all parts of the world.

Today holes can be drilled to depths of 1,500 and 3,000 meters and more. Overburden, regardless of

Figure V-1 — A lighweight, hydraulic core drill easily transportable on the ground or by light plane or helicopter and ready to operate by two man crew. Can drill to 300 m using A size wireline.

tubular steel bit in the face of which are set diamonds (Figure V-3).

This bit, and attached core barrel, are rotated at speed under controlled pressure, by means of hollow, flush-jointed rods, made of steel, through which water is pumped to cool the bit, and remove the rock cuttings.

With the advance of the bit, a cylindrical core of rock passes up into the core barrel where it is held by a core lifter or other means. The circulating water raises the sludge or cuttings to surface outside the rods. This sludge may be collected in a settling box for sampling.

The rods are withdrawn at intervals of 1.5 or 3.0 meters (5 or 10 ft.), and the core is removed from the core barrel for examination and storage. The core and cuttings present a tangible and accurate record of the various formations through which the bit has passed.

The larger drills have recovered cores of up to 100 mm in diameter from depths of more than 4,500 meters (Figure V-11).

depth, no longer presents difficulties, directional holes can now be drilled accurately and wedging of holes is a common undertaking.

The size of the drill core varies with the size of machine used, hole depths and material being drilled. However, the most common sizes are:

A — core diameter 27.0 mm, hole diameter 48.0 mm;

B — core diameter 36.5 mm, hole diameter 60.0 mm;

N — core diameter 47.6 mm, hole diameter 75.7 mm;

H9 — core diameter 63.5 mm, hole diameter 96.0 mm.

Mechanically, the diamond drill consists of a power unit rotating a

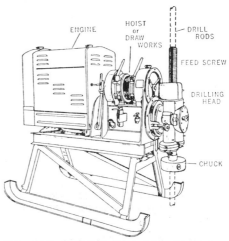

Figure V-2 — Drawing showing the main parts of a standard screw feed diamond drill.

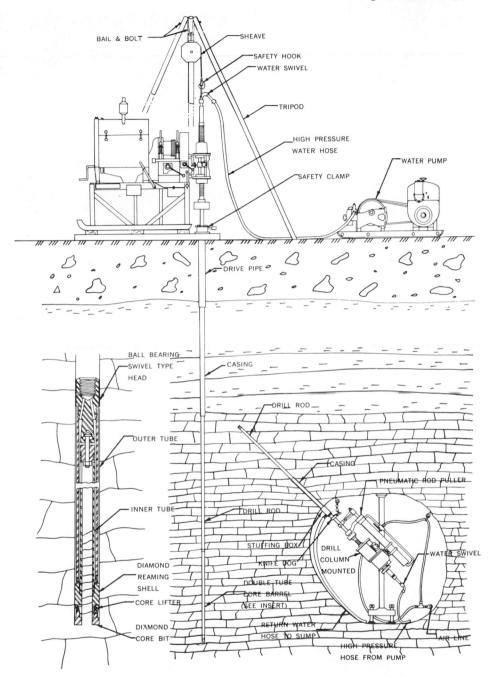

Figure V-3 — Schematic diagram showing diamond drill on surface drilling through overburden into underlying bedrock. The insert at lower left shows the **core barrel** enlarged, while at the right a diamond drill is seen set up underground.

Equipment

The machinery necessary for a drill program consists of the drill itself, with two water and/or mud pumps, together with drill rods, core barrels, casing, pipe and tools (Figure V-3). The drill is a complete unit in itself, consisting of a heavy steel frame upon which is mounted an engine, clutch, transmission to supply power to the hoisting drum and drill head. The drum winds a wire cable running through a sheave wheel at the top of a mast which is disengaged when drilling. The two types of drill heads used employ a mechanical screw feed or a hydraulic feed. At the bottom of the feed mechanism is a two- or three-jawed chuck through which the drill rods pass. The jaws of the chuck are tightened to the rods, which in turn are attached to the core barrel on the end of which is the diamond drill bit, and as the chuck revolves the rods are forced downward.

Figure V-4 — Diamond drill bit set with industrial diamonds, or bortz, with core of rock inside.

Penetrating Overburden

Before drilling can begin, it is necessary to drive a standpipe down through the overburden at whatever angle is desired, until it reaches the ledge rock. The depth and character of the overburden vary in different localities. In some places, it is comparatively shallow, while in others it may be 35 meters or more.

Clay and some forms of sand can be penetrated easily and quickly, but when hardpan, gravel and boulders are encountered, progress is usually slow, regardless of depth. The usual procedure is to drive a 100 mm pipe in sections, with a 160 kilogram drive hammer. While the pipe is being turned slowly with a pair of chain tongs, the hammer strikes the pipe a sharp blow in pile-driver fashion.

If a boulder is encountered, a charge of dynamite is lowered into the hole and detonated. If the boulder is too large to be broken by the explosion on top of it, it may be necessary to drill a hole into it, using the diamond bit. The dynamite is then lowered into the hole and blasted, breaking the rock sufficiently to permit driving the standpipe through it.

When the standpipe reaches bedrock, a second and smaller flush joint casing pipe is lowered inside the larger pipe. Then, to make a tight seal at bedrock to prevent sand and gravel from entering the hole, a large casing bit is used to drill a foot

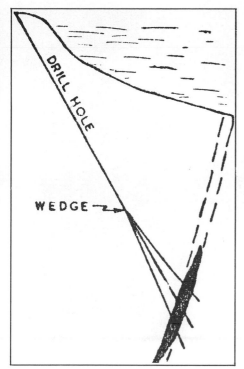

Figure V-5 — Wedging permits getting additional intersections, above or below, or to either side of original intersection.

good for several thousand meters of drilling, while a bit has to be replaced every 15 to 25 meters.

The bit and reaming shell are screwed to the end of a 3 meter core barrel, and lowered through the casing by adding 3 meter sections of drill rod until the bit reaches the bottom of the hole. The top drill rod is attached to the feed screw and chuck. The chuck is then tightened, the water turned on and drilling begins.

The water from the pump passes through the bore and water swivel, then down inside the drill rods, until it reaches the top of the core barrel. It passes between the inner and outer tube of the barrel to the face of the bit and back up on the outside of the rods.

Holes May Require Cementing

If the rock is solid and without fractures, the water will return to the top of the hole where the cuttings or sludge may be collected for sampling purposes or in order to examine the type of rock being penetrated. If the water does not return and it is desired to collect the sludge, cementing of the hole may be necessary. For this purpose, a quick setting cement has been developed which reduces the time lost in this operation materially.

Cementing, too, becomes necessary when caving or blocky ground is encountered, as small pieces of rock may fall into the hole from the walls. Still another use of cementing is for sealing off water seams and faults in a mine, to prevent flooding. This is known as **grouting.** Grouting involves pumping cement under pressure,

or so into the solid rock. The smaller pipe is then driven into this hole.

Drilling The Hole

When **collaring** of the hole has been completed, and the casing cut off at surface to the proper length, the regular operation of diamond drilling commences. For this operation, a 3.0 meter (10 ft.) single or double tube core barrel is used. A bit, set with many small commercial diamonds called **bortz,** is screwed into a reaming shell which fits onto the end of the core barrel. The reaming shell is also set with diamonds which keep the hole up to gauge at all times, thus allowing a new bit to be freely lowered to the bottom of the hole when a worn one has to be replaced. A reaming shell is through a drill hole to fill up the crevices through which the water can flow.

Under ideal drilling conditions and once the bit is lowered to the bottom of the hole and the machine started, the bit will cut a **core,** consisting of a cylindrical piece of rock. Rotating at a high rate of speed, the bit is forced downward by the action of the feed gear on the drill and as it moves down, it pushes the core up into the **core barrel** (Figure V-4).

When the feed screw on the drill has run its full length, the chuck is loosened and run up again. This procedure is continued until the core barrel is filled.

When the core barrel is full, the rods are withdrawn from the hole. These are unscrewed in 6 or 10 metre sections, and stacked against the scaffolding provided for this purpose.

Sometimes, it is desirable to get a second intersection from a single hole. This is done by placing a wedge at some point above the intersection to deflect the bit in another direction. This **wedging** procedure is frequently used in deeper borings, where it can be a real time and money saver (Figure V-5).

The core is placed in core boxes or core trays for examination by the geologist. Interesting sections are split lengthways by a core splitter; half of the section being returned to its place in the core box and the other half sent to the assayer for analysis. The trays or boxes are usually stored on racks in a core shack (Figures V-6, V-7).

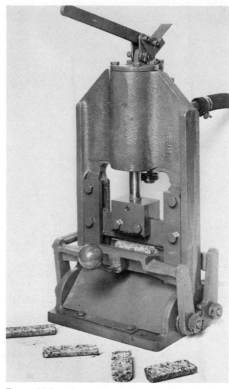

Figure V-6 — A core splitter; one half of split core is used for analysis, remaining half is returned to core box for retention as permanent record.

Wireline Drilling

The **wireline** method, introduced a few years ago, has gained acceptance in the diamond drill industry and most drilling today utilizes this system (Figure V-9).

Drilling is conducted in the same manner as previously described, but the main advantage of wire line drilling is the reduction in rod pulling. When the core barrel is full, or if a blockage occurs, an inner tube containing the core is detached from the core barrel assembly. The tube, and core contained in it, are pulled to the surface by a wire dropped down the line of drill rods. A latch or "overshot assembly" which snaps

Figure V-7 — Removing core from core barrel.

Figure V-8 — Self-propelled, all purpose drill with hydraulic chuck for 3.3 m advance. This machine can recover core, drill rotary or auger holes, or be used for down-the-hole-hammer drilling.

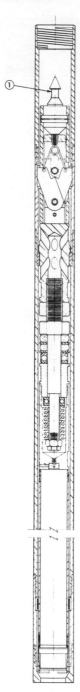

Figure V-9 — A latch or overshot assembly is lowered through the drill rods on a wireline cable to retrieve the inner tube containing the core. The latch snaps onto the cone-shaped pin(1) at the top of the inner tube which is then hoisted to surface through the drill rod string.

onto the top of the inner tube is used for this purpose. The inner tube is rapidly hoisted to surface, within the string of drill rods.

After the core is removed, the inner tube is dropped down into the outer core barrel and drilling resumes. The advantages are particularly evident on deep work, and drilling conditions that allow for good footage per bit. Some of these advantages are: a) Round trip time for retrievable inner barrel is only a fraction of the time for that of a string of drill rods; b) lower round trip time results in reduced "down time", increased net drilling time, more round trips per shift, higher footages per shift; c) less caving in the hole, less blocking; d) longer core runs and higher higher core recovery; e) longer bit life; f) less fatigue for the operator; g) less wear and tear on the drill motor and hoist; h) lower cost per foot of hole drilled.

Other Drilling Methods

With newly designed instruments for analysis continually being developed and the increasing demand for cheaper drilling, new methods of supplying samples have been devised. Recovery of a solid core is now not always an essential requirement.

The **reverse circulation continuous drilling process** is being used successfully in soft to medium-hard formations. The method utilizes a dual tube drill pipe. The drilling fluid, air, or a combination of both, are pumped down between the dual tubing and returned up the inner tube, bringing cuttings from a regular three cone type rotary rock bit (Figure V-12).

Figure V-10 — A bar mounted, underground diamond drill, powered by compressed air, capable of drilling to depth of about 240 m.

Figure V-11 — Modern deep hole, core drilling machine, diesel power, hydraulic feed, capable of reaching depth of 4,500 m. On location in Mackenzie River valley, N.W.T.

Rotary Drilling

Applications for an open hole to lower special instruments is sufficient in some areas to obtain all data required for proper evaluation. A standard rotary drill equipped with necessary compressors and drill pipe is all that is needed for this type of drilling.

Where applicable, cost reduction is significant together with greatly improved productivity.

Underground Diamond Drilling

Extensive diamond drill programs are most important to the operation of an established mine (Figure V-10) where they may be used for:

1) Exploration for new veins and other sources of ore.

2) Outlining and mapping known orebodies and vein systems.

3) Investigating rock types, their structure, and the way they lie, dip or fold.

4) Locating orebodies and veins displaced by faults and folds.

5) Putting out pilot holes to direct drifts and stopes to the proper location.

6) Drain holes, grouting, and ventilation.

Simultaneously with the introduction of hydraulic powered equipment to underground mining, diamond drill manufacturers also developed hydraulic units in combination with air or electric power. The majority of diamond drills underground, however, are air powered. These drills weigh much less than the standard diesel powered surface drills. For instance, a 180 kilogram underground unit

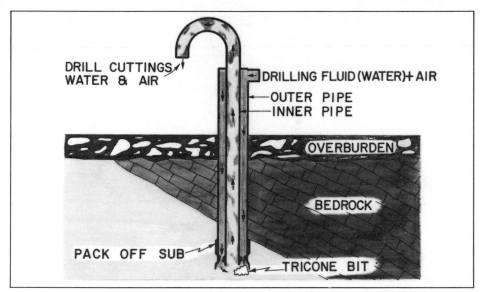

Figure V-12 — Schematic outline of dual tube process used in reverse circulation rotary drilling.

can drill "A" core with a hole diameter of 48.0 mm to depths of up to 175 meters. On the other hand, a surface unit would weigh roughly 1,100 to 1,400 kilograms, excluding the towers and accessories, fuel supplies, water lines, and the equipment and supplies necessary for moving, cutting rods and building camps.

Because of the lighter equipment, the relative ease of setting up, and the fact that water and other sevices are already installed, the number of hours of effective drilling is greatly increased for the underground driller.

Underground diamond drilling machines are made up of a power unit, a drive train, a hoist and/or an air puller and a swivel head. Some of the other equipment required includes pumps, rods, core barrels, and bits.

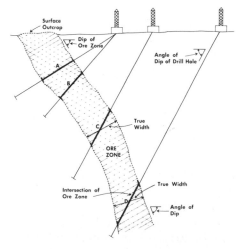

Figure V-13 — A section through a potential orebody showing its outline as inferred from four diamond drill holes. Note that only at A and B does the intersection represent the true width of the orebody; the true width at C or D is found by adjusting the length of the intersection by its angle to the assumed dip of the ore. By drilling on a number of sections roughly parallel to this one, a three-dimensional picture is built up from which an estimate of tonnage and overall grade can be computed.

Figure V-14 — Drilling from the ice on northern lake.

The underground location permits the drilling of holes at any angle and this is very advantageous to the mine geologist.

Power units

Air powered motors are used extensively underground and require a supply of clean, dry air at the correct volume and pressure to ensure good performance. An air motor in good condition will continue to deliver almost full torque capacity, even when operating at slow speed.

There are two types of air motors — the piston type and the vane type. The piston air motor has a positive displacement and will generally still function at a low air pressure. It has a lower consumption of air per horse power, but is more complicated

mechanically. The vane type motor is lighter than the piston type and is simpler mechanically. It allows more air to escape and is subject to stall under load when the air pressure is low. Also, it is noiser than the piston type.

Electric motors are also used underground for long term drilling projects where a suitable power supply is available. These operate at near constant speed so that the complementary hydraulic equipment gives good control over the drilling operation.

Diesel engines are also used on heavier units, in areas where there is no, or a shortage of, air supply. Although a good source of power, they are heavy and bulky and necessitate extra ventilation and attached **scrubbers.**

CHAPTER VI

Sampling Determines Value

The estimation of the value of an orebody rests on two mutually-inclusive features — quality, which leads to determinations of average or unit value, and quantity or tonnage.

Of these, the quantity is a function of volume combined with density and as such is relatively easily determined. Although this is true, the economic or commerical tonnage must take into account the unit or average values, or qualities, of the ore as revealed by sampling and analysis. It must also take into account the manner in which the valuable mineral is distributed through the orebody, and in previous chapters it has been made clear that a high degree of uniformity is quite rare. This gives rise to one of the engineer's main obsessions, and which occupies a great deal of his attention throughout the life of an orebody, from raw prospect through production, namely, sampling.

Sampling is the act or process of taking for analysis representative portions of the mass under consideration. The analysis itself returns information on the quality *of that particular sample.* As a general rule, the best estimate of the average value of an orebody is found by taking a large number of small samples from various portions of the orebody, and combining the assay results by **weighting** with various linear measurements. Actually, sampling affects virtually all aspects of human endeavour, and the reader will be familiar with consumer market research, which rests on the art of sampling and involves much the same kind of interpretive techniques. Sometimes, a sampling program on a large low grade ore deposit will require highly sophisticated statistical techniques.

Grab Samples Not Representative

The first samples that are usually taken from a showing that outcrops at or near surface are **grab samples.** These are simply random pieces of rock selected from the site to determine whether or not they contain any portion of the metal or mineral sought. They should be regarded as single samples, and as such do not necessarily relate to the average grade of the whole body.

Upon the demonstration of worthwhile, or significant, amounts of metal in such grab samples, surface work is then undertaken. The vein or deposit is exposed as fully as possible, following which representative surface samples are taken or cut, generally under the close supervision of an engineer.

These samples are known, as **channel samples,** since they are really small trenches or channels, cut by hammer and rock chisel, or **moil,** across the supposed orebody at regular intervals.

Chip channels are sometimes taken by the engineer to get a quick approximation of contained value. These consist of random pieces quickly knocked off the outcrop with an effort made to take representative amounts. They cannot be fully relied upon, so normally do not enter final mathematical calculations.

The desirable but, alas, too infrequent surface channel is a cut about four inches wide and one-half inch deep across the supposed ore zone, the chips and material removed being carefully collected, marked and bagged for analysis.

Sample At Close Intervals

It is customary not to cut too long a channel, one-metre lengths being the maximum generally preferred, since the engineer at this point will wish to know where the valuable metal is. That is, he would want to know whether the metal shows any preference for foot or hanging wall sides, whether there are pay-streaks, or whether the orebody is relatively homogeneous. Thus the margins or limits of values are discovered. It is good practice to extend the channels into the walls far enough to entirely delimit values.

It is highly desirable, but not often practicable, to space surface channels at regular intervals along the vein, as this obviates one mathematical calculation in their interpretation.

As a final check, it is sometimes desirable to collect a **bulk sample,** which either combines channel rejects, or is a considerably larger portion of the whole. A bulk sample may range from a few hundred pounds to several tons in weight.

After all possible surface samples are taken, they are analyzed (assayed) and laid out to scale on a map for study and calculation. As the exposed surface allows visual inspection and study of two of the three dimensions of any orebody, these samples are highly significant. The maps are called **assay maps** and show visually the result of analysis of each sample, and its location in relation to every other sample.

Assay Maps Important

Since assay maps are the best collection of facts available, their importance cannot be over-estimated.

In order to arrive at an average value, and to delimit areas that are possible of economic extraction, the engineer interprets the results produced, outlining on the map the best areas. It is here that experience is essential, and too often sacrificed to hope and expectation.

Within these limits of area, samples are then **weighted;** that is, the value of each sample is assigned to the portion of the vein that it represents.

Before assessing or averaging assay values, it is customary to **cut** any high values. This is done by either of two generally accepted methods.

In the common empirical method of cutting assays, a direct average is taken off without changing any figures. This is called the **uncut** figure — and if enough samples have been taken, it should, in theory, approach accuracy. It is customary, however, to re-average the whole at this stage, and replace every value higher than the uncut figure arrived at above with that figure. The result of this is called the **average-re-average** figure, and is conceded to represent the minimum grade expectancy.

In the second method, an average is taken off in which all values above an empirical figure are reduced to that figure. As this method is arbitrary, and entirely dependent upon judgment, it is a questionable one except in areas for which such empirical figures have been established by years of experience.

Usually, two, three, or even more, mathematical methods will be tried in arriving at an average. Then if comparable results are had in several, the approximate figure will be accepted.

It is obvious that one high assay surrounded by many low ones has little significance. Frequency of high assays is a considerable factor, but occasional high assays, called **erratics,** are to be looked on with caution and, in many instances, eliminated entirely or drastically reduced.

Assays are, of course, weighted for their representation and relation of width and length. An assay of X units per ton, for instance, could represent a grab sample, or small piece taken at random. But it might represent the result obtained by analysis of a channel carefully cut. In the latter case, it will represent a width — usually given in metres and tenths of metres for ease of calcuation — and be expressed as say, X units across Y metres. This indicates that the average content of metal is X units per ton across Y metres of average material, measured across the orebody.

Figure VI-1 — Splitting diamond drill core. Sample constituting one half will be assayed, the remaining half will be returned to core box for future reference.

In weighting samples the XY pairs are multiplied, and a sum taken of their series. This is divided by the sum of the Y values to give a **weighted** average across the section. This process is carried further by applying the distances between adjacent parallel sections as another kind of weighting factor, and so a geometric average over an area may be computed. Carrying it still further, the distance between parallel areas can be applied as still other weighting factors, ultimately to produce the average metal content, or other expression of quality, throughout the volume of the orebody. It will be noted that the weighting factors are all linear or area dimensions, and these combine to give volume. By applying a density factor to the volume, a figure for the tonnage involved will be obtained.

Until the growing adoption of the metric system, gold, silver, and other precious metal assays have been expressed in terms of decimals of troy ounces per ton, as say 0.38 oz. per ton. The new unit for the precious metals is **grams per metric ton,** and 0.38 oz. per ton would become expressed as 13.03 **grams per tonne.**

Analyses of base metals, uranium, and most others are expressed in terms of simple percentage, or in percentage units. In the metric system, 1 per cent would mean 1/100 part of a metric ton (tonne), or ten kilograms (22.046 lb.). (In English units, 1% of a short ton would be equivalent to 20 lb.) For trading, or business purposes, the metal content is often translated to money values, but caution must be exercised, as will be discussed in a later chapter.

Drilling Gives Third Dimension

After surface sampling indicates a possible orebody, or concentration of valuable mineral, diamond drilling is undertaken. This is a sampling method by which portions of the orebody at depth are removed by taking out a **core** for inspection and analysis.

Where radioactive minerals are sought, it is customary to check the core with a spectrometer to determine the most interesting sections.

Sludge samples are also taken while drilling and are the collected cuttings made by the drill. These are useful as checks against the drill core samples.

Cores are **logged,** or described in detail, and may or may not be split for analysis. Splitting of core is done so that the remaining half can be studied in conjunction with the known analysis of the opposing section, or in order that some later inspection can be made (Figure VI-1).

Diamond drilling adds the remaining dimension — depth — to the three dimensions required for accurate volumetric determination.

Sampling of the core, therefore, will indicate continuity of values to the depth drilled.

Engineers disagree as to the reliance to be placed upon the assays of core samples. One group will accept them without reservation, while the more conservative will accept them only as indications of possible value, it being argued that the actual volume of rock as represented by the core is so small a portion of the whole as to render it questionable.

It would be difficult to give any hard and fast rule, for the type and character of the orebody have a great influence on the degree to which the

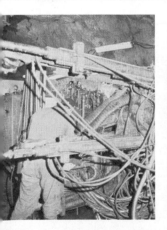

EXPLORATION (top): Geologist examines drill core; helicopter services field party. TRANSPORTATION (second from top): Underground by load-haul-dump machine, on surface by train. IN THE MINE (third from top): Drill Jumbo; ventilation fans; lunch room. Bottom: Texasgulf surface plant, near Timmins, Ontario; open pit in background.

OPEN PIT MINING (top): 200-ton capacity monster dwarfs half-ton pickup; rotary drill; power shovel loads truck. (Second from top): Ball mills grind ore; copper flotation. SMELTING (third from top): Dumping slag; copper wirebars ready for shipment. MILLING (bottom): Control room; leaching uranium.

results may be accepted. It can be said, however, that if the assays from core samples are relatively consistent — more especially where a good deal of surface or visual imformation has been collected — considerable confidence can be placed in them.

Salting is a Risk

In both surface and drill sampling, **salting** — influencing the results by introduction of foreign material — is a possible risk, as it is during these stages that decisions are made involving large expenditures. Salting can be either voluntary, or involuntary.

Voluntary, or premeditated, salting is, of course, the stratagem of scoundrels, but equally culpable and equally serious, is the involuntary form by which perfectly honest but misguided individuals unknowingly affect results.

Involuntary salting is the more common, and results when the engineer or sampler leaves out areas or sections which he does not think will run, but which may do so. This form is more prevalent than might be expected, and can be rectified only by meticulous and thorough workmanship. The eye cannot assay.

Underground Sampling Methods

Based upon the information now collected, and carefully studied, underground development is undertaken.

Underground samples are usually of two types — channel or muck. Underground channels are taken in exactly the same manner as surface channels, except that, for

convenience, they are taken at the **face** — the advancing end of a drift or crosscut — or at the **back** or roof. It is customary to take both as checks. Where the opening, or drift, runs with the ore — drifts with it — such channels are known as **face** and **back samples.** Should the exploratory opening cross the zone — as in a crosscut — or should the ore exceed the opening in width, channel samples taken along the side to cut the possible ore at right angles are known as **rib samples.** All channel samples should be taken as nearly as possible across the ore zone.

Figure VI-2 — Engineer collects chip sample.

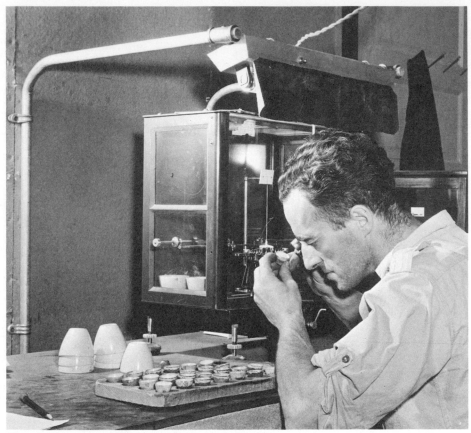

Figure VI-3 — Assayer examines gold bead before weighing.

Channel samples are also taken later during the mining of the orebody. These are from stopes or other mining areas and are known as **breast** or **stope samples.** All such samples are mapped and recorded, producing a constant guide for ore removal.

While there is an economic limit to the amount of time and money which can be devoted to production sampling, as a general rule, the more samples that are taken the more efficient and complete is the extraction of ore. It is often impossible to go back and mine ore that has been left behind.

Car and **muck samples** are taken from broken ore as it moves to the mill. Usually these are taken by the workman as cars are filled. They consist of taking a small amount of muck, i.e., broken ore or rock, from each car, or some other specific volume at regular intervals. Regular interval could mean from, say, every fifth or tenth car, but always the same interval, whatever is adopted.

Muck samples can be used to check the average grade of millfeed. In fact, they are often considered to be the most reliable samples for grade estimation.

It has frequently been observed that muck samples from a mine,

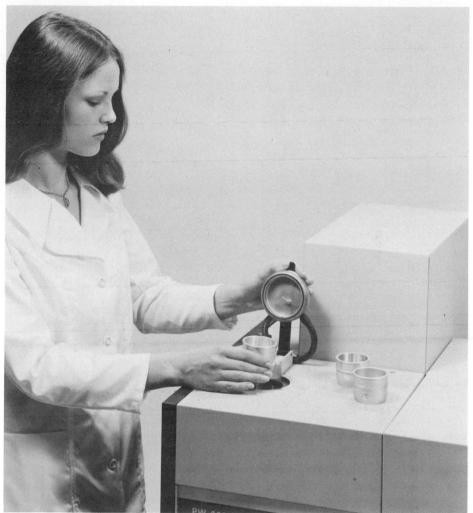

Figure VI-4 — Placing a sample in the spectrometer for analysis.

averaged over a year, will coincide almost exactly with the actual value of the mill production plus tailings loss as determined by sampling.

Sampling In The Mill

At the mill head, usually after crushing but before grinding, a **mill head sample** is taken by a mechanical sampler. This machine cuts out a portion of the feed at regular intervals and again provides a determination of the whole.

The study of all the above samples will tell the mine manager the average grade that is delivered to the mill at all times.

By accurately weighing the volume sent to the mill, the total metallic or mineral content is determined.

In the process of milling, or extraction of desired product, samples are taken at all significant points. These serve to guide the mill

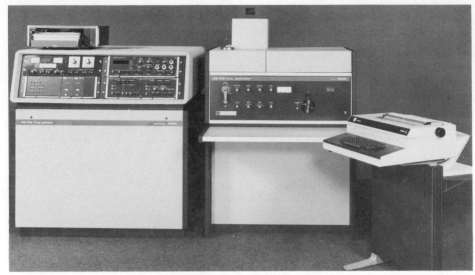

Figure VI-5 — A semi-automatic sequential spectrometer, the Philips PW 1410. In this machine the sample of ore or other material is irradiated by an X-ray beam causing it to give off a secondary radiation which can be measured to determine the various contained elements and their amount.

operator in controlling the treatment process and chemical requirements. At the end of the milling procedure a **tailings sample** is taken, the difference between the average heads sample and the tailings sample representing the recovery effected.

The final product itself is also sampled in order to determine its unit value, and the importance of this is obvious. The product may be bullion, as in the case of a gold or a silver mine, or it may be one or more concentrates of metallic sulphides or oxides which are to be shipped to a smelter.

The process of sampling does not stop there, for the purchaser, whether it be the Mint, a smelter, or some other processor, will also take samples of the material and base the payment on the results. At this point it is also usual to have an independent sample taken, known as an **umpire sample,** which may be used as a final basis of settlement

between buyer and seller if they cannot agree between themselves.

The entire process is thus the determination of the whole by littles, a progressive refinement of method, and, finally, the analysis of increasing volumes. The final and determinative sample is, of course, the treatment of the whole mass, from which there is no rebuttal.

It is thus seen that sampling carries far beyond the initial prospect stage, forming an important part of all phases of mining and milling.

Routine operation of a mine calls for a large amount of sampling and assaying. As an example, one large gold mine which mined and milled some 4,100 tonnes of ore per day, ran some 276,000 assays per year in its laboratory, or an average of 750 each day. The samples were obtained from many different operations in its mine and milling process.

CHAPTER VII

Mining
the Ore

While the layman may invest or speculate in the shares of mining companies and prospects, he rarely gets an opportunity to visit a property or see the design of operations. Often technical terms are used in connection with news and developments which the average person does not understand.

There are wide variations among mines, in terms of scale of operation, the attitudes and shapes of the orebodies and veins, the material strengths of its ore components and wall rocks, and in the manner in which the valuable minerals are disseminated.

In size, they may range from small operations with but a few levels, to large ones extending to great depths and containing literally hundreds of kilometers of workings. For instance, the great Hollinger gold mine after nearly sixty years of productive life had about 560 km of shafts, crosscuts, drifts, and raises. These openings are referred to as "narrow workings" and will be defined a little further on.

Opening and developing a mine is a costly business. The primary opening is a shaft, usually vertical but sometimes inclined, and the simplest costs upwards of a thousand dollars per meter. Crosscuts and drifts are costed in

terms of hundreds of dollars per meter. Raises, which are placed for a variety of purposes, are proportionately expensive.

The expenses involved in the development of a mine demand that the utmost care be taken in planning. Thus, mining companies carry out a great deal of detailed drilling and other exploratory work so that the ultimate operation will be as economic as possible, consistent with the character of the orebodies.

This chapter includes a cross-sectional sketch of the underground and surface workings of a hypothetical mine, which reasonably illustrates a modestly sized operation on a steep-dipping vein in a Precambrian area. It shows graphically the range of principal steps that have to be taken, and helps to explain a number of the more common mining terms (Figure VII-1).

Ore In Place

The virgin ore is **in place** in the vein or orebody. In the production process it is drilled and blasted; transported through stopes, chutes and raises, crushed underground; hoisted from the depths; crushed again on surface; then conveyed to the mill for recovery processing.

In the sketch three common types of stope operations are enlarged for

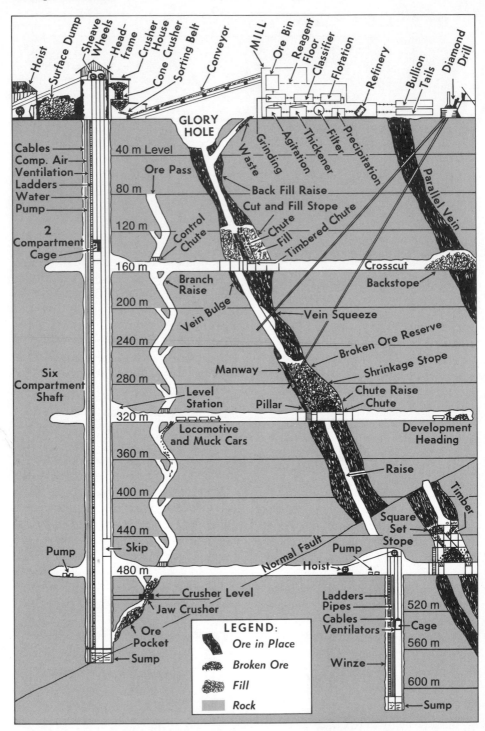

Figure VII-1 — Sketch of idealized section through the workings of a typical mine.

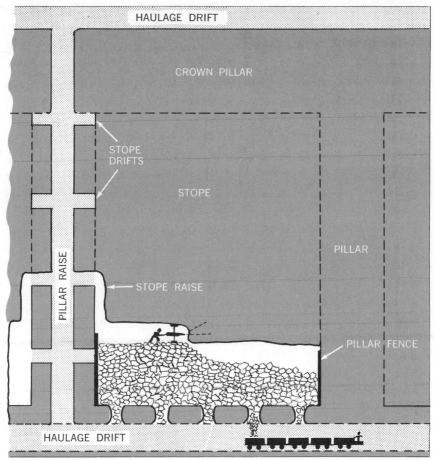

Figure VII-2 — Section of a typical longitudinal shrinkage stope, formerly a very common method but not greatly used now.

clearer presentation. Level details are only given at every fourth horizon. The horizontal scale is greatly enlarged, here again to enable detail to be given.

It must be understood that the general layout is an ideal one designed for a hypothetical case, in order to give the layman an approximate idea of the workings of a mine. The mining expert will understand that the picture of the vein or ore structure only gradually unfolds — usually with many surprises — and actual mine design is accordingly flexible.

The sketch has been made with a view to conveying only the broader view of the operation, not preciseness of detail. It does not represent a true section, as many of the workings and structures are not in the same plane as, say, the shaft. But in order to convey the complete picture, everything has been resolved to the one section, so this must be kept in mind. Drifts, for instance, run at right angles to the sketch section, parallel to and usually along the vein; they are similar to crosscuts in the way they are driven.

While definitions of most of the common mining terms are appended, the following explanatory notes will make their meaning more clear.

Ore Reserves Defined

Ore may be defined as rock carrying mineral values which can be extracted and marketed *at a profit.*

Figure VII-3 — The shaft collar where the miners board the cage for transportation to the levels underground in the mine.

Thus in the case of a mineral bearing vein, if the average value of a sufficient tonnage is such that a profit is indicated, then the vein filling is called ore. Otherwise, it is just vein filling. In terms of definitions for our present purpose, vein, lode, orebody are synonymous. The values may extend into the adjacent wallrock but the definition still holds.

Ore-in-place, then, would be the orebody as is, before any of it is broken. **Ore reserves** would be ore-in-place that has been sufficiently developed by means of drifts and raises in it, or crosscuts through it, to establish the grade and tonnage with reasonable certainty. **Broken ore** reserves are contained in stopes after breaking and are demonstrated in the shrinkage stope shown in the sketch. But, these reserves might also be stored in other underground workings or on the surface dump.

The ore veins in the example are shown to have a similar angle of dip and are assumed to have the same strike, although this cannot be depicted in a section. The two veins shown are parallel occurrences.

The **dip** is the angle which the vein makes with the horizontal when measured at right angles to its strike. The **strike** of the vein is its longitudinal direction taken in a horizontal plane.

The **wallrock** is that rock adjacent to the vein and is usually distinguished as the **hangingwall** on the upper side and the **footwall** on the under side.

Among the more common structural conditions encountered in a mine is **faulting.** This may have occurred before the veins were formed, in which case it is called **pre-ore faulting,** or after the vein was formed, when it is known as **post-ore faulting.** The latter is often quite bothersome for large blocks of ground are shifted which may contain the sections of the vein being mined. The sketch shows what is called a **normal fault** which took place after the vein had intruded the rock. It is called "normal" because the lower block has moved up in relation to the upper block. If the movement had been in the opposite direction it

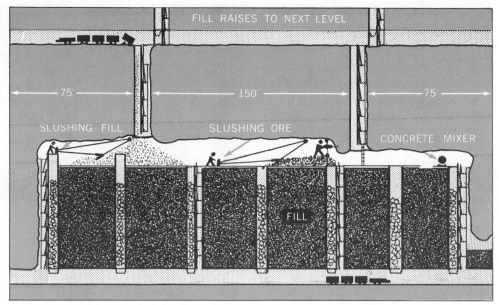

Figure VII-4 — Flat back longitudinal cut-and-fill stope. Note that ore removal and filling are taking place simultaneously on the same floor.

would be called a **reverse fault.**
Evidence of the fault is revealed in
the levels, crosscuts, the main shaft,
and by the shift of the vein.

Much Preliminary Work

A vein in most cases is an intrusive
from below into the prevailing
country rock, along some structural
weakness. The vein filling is often
quartz or carbonate with rock
inclusions. It may or may not carry
gold or other minerals. While many
geological theories are held as to
how the minerals come to be there,
the important thing is that they are
there and that they have been found.

Although base metal deposits
sometimes occur in veins, they are
more likely to be found as irregular
bodies of mineralization
concentrated in a particular area due
to some structural coincidence such
as faulting, shear zones, or some other
geological feature. The porphyry
copper deposits of the western

United States, for instance, are huge
masses whose dimensions are
measured in the hundreds of metres.
At Sudbury, the sulphide minerals
associated with the valuable nickel,
copper and precious metals occur in
bodies that might be hundreds of
metres in length and tens of metres
in width.

Before ore can be mined
underground, a lot of preliminary
work must be accomplished, But
before any underground work is
started, the continuity of the vein or
deposit at depth is probably first
confirmed by putting down some
diamond drill holes as shown.
On account of bulging,
squeezing and the general
irregularity of veins, the
interpretation of the intersections
must be carefully studied. Any core
that looks interesting is assayed and
mineralized sections **logged,** or
recorded with particular care
(Figure VI-1).

Then a **shaft** of suitable size is sunk and **levels** established at say, intervals of 50 meters. At the various working levels a shaft **station** is cut for entry and exit purposes. It also provides storage space for material and equipment and is simply a large opening tapering down to the crosscut size of 3 x 3 m.

Shafts, crosscuts, drifts, and raises are referred to as **narrow workings** in that they are advanced by blasting in such a way that the completed opening maintains a given cross-section throughout its length, and are "narrow" in cross-section relative to their length.

Figure VII-5 — Right, a stoper at Inco's Thompson mine drills hole for inserting rock bolt, six feet in length, to help support the rock in the back. A metal screen held up by the bolts also protects workers from small pieces of rock that may be jarred loose by blasting. On the left a driller uses a jackleg drill to drill a hole for blasting ore.

The **crosscut** is driven as a development heading to intersect the veins and explore for others. When a vein or ore bearing structure is cut in a crosscut, **drifts** are driven along it. Drifts and crosscuts are similar tunnel openings, the difference being their direction relative to the structure. Both are referred to as development headings.

Raises are openings driven up the deposit from level to level at intervals. They develop or indicate the ore grade and tonnage that may be expected, but are later used to service the stope that will be started, or for backfill purposes. Some raises are driven adjacent to ore for access, supply, service or ventilation purposes.

The **stope** is the productive workshop of the mine where the ore is first broken for transportation to the mill. In the section illustrated, three common stope methods of extracting the ore are shown, namely cut-and-fill, shrinkage, and square-set. There are numerous other stope methods, as well as variations and combinations of the different methods. Some of the more common stoping methods will be described below.

While the miner's tasks are not light ones, Canadian mining practices have become highly mechanized in all aspects, especially in drilling, rock handling, in the driving of drifts and raises, and even in shaft sinking. In drilling, lightweight fast-drilling machines equipped with tungsten-carbide-tipped bits have taken over from the heavier ones formerly in use, except for certain specialized heavy-duty jobs. In ore handling, a wide variety

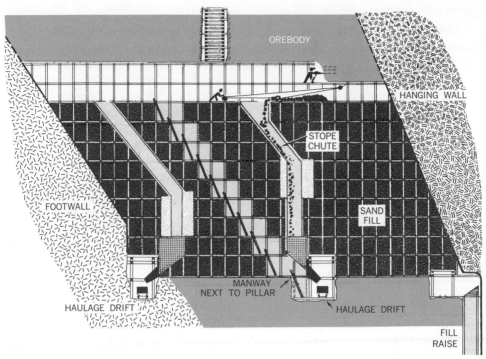

Figure VII-6 — Standard square set stope mined across the width of the orebody. The manway and fill raise are actually situated in pillar which separates adjoining stopes. The pillars are mined subsequently.

of loaders and haulers have become available, and the hand shovel is quite the thing of the past. For raise driving, whereas in former times the miner had to climb an awkward chain ladder with his equipment, we now have a climbing machine which operates on a monorail, and so here again little muscular energy is involved. An increasing number of raises are reamed from a pilot diamond drill hole, using a special tool. In shaft sinking, the last of the really fatiguing toil has been removed by the successful development of special digging machines. There are now also drilling machines which bore shafts as large as three or more metres in diameter. In all, underground mining is now no more physically

demanding than, say, work on highway or other well-organized construction.

Stoping Methods

The safety of the miner is the paramount consideration in selecting a suitable stoping method. Even then, constant care must be taken and he must be ever on his guard against loose rock. So as soon as he enters a stope, he must examine the back carefully, bringing down any overhanging loose rock with the aid of a scaling bar (Figure VII-7).

As mentioned, the first requirement of a stoping method is the safety of the miners. In the organization of a stope there must also be means of access for the

Figure VII-7 — Miner using steel scaling bar to pry rock, loosened by blasting, from back and walls of stope.

great many mines use tailings from the milling process, after removing the slimes, that is the portion that has been ground exceptionally fine.

Stopes are started from principal levels, and at this point the operation is frequently known as **silling.** Depending on many factors, the **sill** may consist of a timber structure placed in a section of a drift which has had a slice taken out of its **back,** which is the miner's term for "ceiling." This structure will include **chutes** spotted throughout its length for the removal of the broken ore from the stope which will be developed above. It will also include the beginnings of the **manways** which must be maintained for access and for services such as compressed air, water, and electricity. Other means of silling may substitute a series of short raises or **box holes** for the timber structure, and these will be placed at short intervals along the strike of the drift, or in the footwall parallel to it. The development for some stoping methods calls for a rather elaborate system of box holes, drawing ore from scraper drifts, which in turn are fed from drawpoints underlying a fairly extensive stope. Stope development may include rib pillars, and pillars overlying the main haulageway. In any case, we have now provided the prime requirements of access, ore removal, service, and supply.

miners to reach their working places, means of removing the broken ore produced, means of access for supplies of tools, explosives, timber, equipment, and perhaps filling material. Ventilating air must also be provided on a continuous basis.

Backfill may be waste rock, sand, or gravel which is used to fill the voids created by stoping, and thus give support to wall areas. It may be placed immediately during the mining operation, as in cut-and-fill or square-set stoping, or it may be placed at a later time. It is used for safety, and also for economic reasons, the latter where wall conditions are such that it is impossible to **mine clean.** That is, where low grade or barren material finds its way into the ore stream in unacceptable amounts. Nowadays, a

Shrinkage Stoping

Shrinkage stoping consists of taking successive horizontal slices, usually about three meters high, throughout the length of the stope (Figure VII-2). On being fragmented in blasting,

Figure VII-8 — Drilling blastholes for sublevel caving at mine in Sudbury district, Ontario. This rig drills holes up to 12 m in length in fan shaped pattern to break off five-foot slices of ore. The console has a dial to guide the driller in setting the incline of the two drills.

the ore will acquire spaces between the broken particles so that a cubic metre of it measured in the solid will now occupy a little more than one-and-a-half cubic meters. In order to maintain working room, about one-third of it must be drawn from the chutes, thus "shrinking" the volume of broken ore.

This process is continued upward until the stope either reaches the level next above, or is topped at some pre-determined elevation, leaving a horizontal pillar to be removed at a later time.

At this point, there is left a large store or magazine of broken ore, and the reader may be interested in knowing that in places like Sweden, France, and Russia, the method is known as "magazine" stoping.

As there is no provision for artificial support, and as the removal of broken ore is entirely dependent on gravity, it is obvious that the method is applicable only in steep-dipping deposits, with strong and competent ore and wall rocks.

Cut-and-Fill Stoping

Conditions of weak wall rocks, or higher ground pressures with increasing depth, may call for the adoption of cut-and-fill stoping (Figure VII-4). As there is an added operation, that of filling the void

Figure VII-9 — A load-haul-dump machine with its 5-yard bucket loaded with six tons of broken ore moves along haulageway to ore pass.

space left by the mining of each slice, it is obviously more expensive than is shrinkage stoping but is not proportionately so.

As each slice is blasted onto a floor, which nowadays is often a mixture of cement and de-slimed mill tailings, the ore is removed to the stope millholes leading to the chutes in the haulageway below; this leaves a space about six or seven metres high throughout the length and width of the stope. After provision has been made for the extension of the millhole and manway structures, filling material is run in, usually waste rock or treated mill tailings piped in as a pulp. The contained water in the tailings is allowed to decant and to percolate down through the previous layers of fill.

An advantage of this method is that it makes for clean mining with little dilution. With a competent ore rock, it is also quite safe. Furthermore, it is selective, and can accommmodate various geological vagaries much better than can shrinkage stoping.

The process of taking slice after slice is repeated until the level above is reached, or to some pre-determined pillar line.

Square-Set Stoping

Square-set stoping is no longer much used as it depends upon a large supply of timber which has become very expensive. It is of interest, however, in that it can be applied to almost any condition of rock, and one could say that if a given orebody cannot be mined by square-setting, it cannot be mined at all.

Square-set stoping is a system in which just enough ore is blasted out at a time to make room for one timber set about 1.5 m x 1.5 m x 2.3 m in size. This set is placed immediately after the block of ore has been blasted and fallen to the floor of the line of sets next below, which are ultimately backfilled. The removal of broken ore is done through millholes formed by lining selected lines of sets in an upward direction. Stope access is provided through manways constructed in a similar way (Figure VII-6).

The sets can be extended in any direction, and this provides for excellent flexibility with regard to geological conditions, and for very clean mining. Considering the labor required for timbering and backfilling, and the present-day cost of timber, the method is obviously suited only to high grade deposits. Its description is given here simply to demonstrate the ingenuity of miners.

Figure VII-10 — Conventional blasthole open stope as employed at Whalesback mine, Newfoundland.

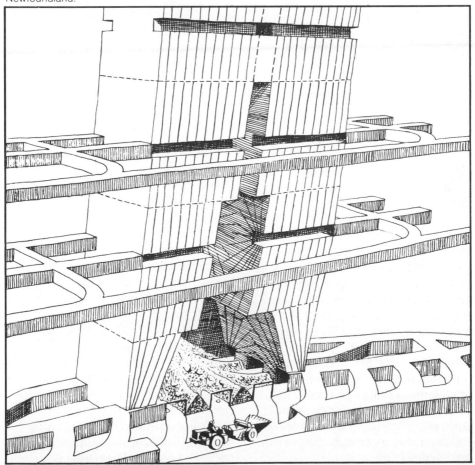

Figure VII-11 — Mine geologist (centre) discusses development progress with operators of Alimak raise machine at Hudson Bay Mining and Smelting Co., Flin Flon, Manitoba.

Sub-Level Blast Hole Stoping

One stoping method is a peculiarly Canadian development, though as a family, it has been adopted in many parts of the world, and is referred to as **sub-level blast hole stoping.** It began forty-odd years ago with a rather suddenly-found ability to drill holes in rocks up to thirty metres in length, at costs low enough for them to be used as blast holes in excavation work. In its original form these blast holes were put down with diamond drills, but over the years percussion drills have been developed which, in conjunction with tungsten-carbide bits, have the capacity for drilling blast holes up to 30 meters or more at high levels of efficiency (Figure VII-8).

The method has many variants, depending upon the sizes and attitudes of the orebodies, but it is applied principally to the underground mining of large orebodies, whose wall rocks are competent in that they will stand without support over considerable spans of excavation. Large underground structures, such as hydroelectric stations, are built in excavations which are essentially derivations of the methods of this procedure. The method is quite safe, and accounts for a considerable part of Canada's underground ore production.

One example of this kind of stoping is illustrated in Figure VII-10. The block is prepared by driving sub-drifts along both walls of the orebody, or along selected pillar lines as the case may be, at vertical intervals of about 20 meters. From the sub-drifts, blast holes are drilled on radial patterns extending out into the block. These sets of holes are placed at regular spacings, so that they describe slices of about two meters in thickness. The sets of holes making up a slice extending over the entire face of the stope are charged and fired as required, and each such slice will produce thousands of tons of ore. The operation is carried out in such a way as to follow a line of retreat, commonly to a service pillar at the end of the block.

All variants of the method have the feature of co-planar sets of blast holes which describe slices, and their planes may be laid out at any convenient attitude, depending upon that of the orebody itself.

The broken ore is removed by L-H-D machines from mucking drawpoints, as illustrated, at the end of short crosscuts driven into the ore zone (Figure VII-10).

Open Pit Operation

Sometimes in the early stages of mining an orebody it may be suited to mining by **open pit** (also known as **open cut** or **open cast** mining) at the surface, provided that conditions of lateral extent and shallow overburden are met. In fact, open pit operations have become very important in Canadian mining, and account for many thousands of daily tons in the production of iron ore, asbestos, copper, molybdenum, cement rock, limestone, and several others. Where a large scale of operation is justified, open pit mining offers the advantages of the highest degrees of mechanization, with large drilling, loading, and hauling equipment units (Figures VII-14, VII-18).

Although on first appearance an open pit operation may look simple, in its engineering and economic aspects it is anything but that, and it calls for close planning in minute detail before any excavation takes place. In one way, planning is done from the bottom up, after first ascertaining the bottom economic limit of the pit operation, and this in

Figure VII-12 — L-H-D machine dumps its 6-ton load into an ore pass. Like other diesel-powered underground equipment, the machine is fitted with an oxy-catalytic scrubber to remove objectionable exhaust fumes.

Figure VII-13 — Inco's Pipe open pit mine, 35 km south of Thompson, Manitoba.

itself calls for the best in engineering acumen and experience. As shown in sketch (Fig. VII-15) a safe pit slope must be maintained, and this always involves the excavation of the upper **benches** beyond the ore limits and into the waste rocks of the walls, such waste being disposed of to dumps provided for. So, the question of the waste-to-ore ratio is always before the planning engineer, and keeps intruding into the economic aspects of the operation. Especially in lower grade ores, where profit margins are small, expert planning is essential if the apparent benefits are to be derived.

Other Mining Methods

There are literally dozens of mining methods in use today, but we have described here the principal ones used in Canadian underground and surface mining. In any case, most methods are fairly close relatives to these. Surface mining includes open pit metal mines, stream and lake dredging, and also coal stripping mines which now constitute an important segment of western Canadian mining.

But mining does not stand still, and the reader will from time to time have his curiosity aroused by mention of methods which are still rather exotic, but which can become realities in the proper circumstances.

One of these is **solution mining** in which solvents of appropriate chemical composition would be injected through adequately-placed drill holes to dissolve the valuable mineral; the solutions are then recovered through other drill holes for the extraction of their metals. There has even been speculation as to the feasibility of using nuclear blasting to fracture the ore zones in such a way as to make them more permeable to the solvents. While a body of research is being carried out by large mining companies, and while there appear to be serious problems, it is not beyond possibility that coming years may see some results. In Northern Ontario, a solution mining technique is being employed at Kerr Addison's Agnew Lake uranium mine where acidic solutions are percolated through the broken ore in the stopes to dissolve the uranium.

There is also the matter of mining the **ocean floors** for the nodular deposits of manganese, nickel, copper, cobalt, and other metals which cover vast areas. These are usually situated at great depths, and this will immediately suggest serious technical problems. There are, too, problems in international law as to the ownership of various areas, a subject that has been discussed at a number of international conferences. A consortium, in which Inco Limited is a partner, has concluded successful tests for recovery of the metal-bearing nodules from the sea floor, but the economics of a production program will be governed by metal demand and the anticipated costs of extraction (Figure XI-3).

Stope and Mine Control

In addition to labour supervision, every mine is dependent on an engineering and geological office for production control and layout. All development openings must be surveyed and their proper directions determined; any one stope is often a fairly complex structure. Volumes of ore mined must be measured at regular intervals, for tonnage checks, and for the determination of incentive bonuses. The geological department must keep up-to-date maps and sections of the orebodies, and direct an ever-continuing underground exploration program.

A large amount of sampling must be carried out in development headings and in stopes, and in a large

Figure VII-14 — Big rotary drill used for drilling holes for blasting in open pit.

mine this effort will provide literally hundreds of samples for assaying each day. The results are used as guides and checks on production, and in one important sense they are analogous to quality control in any industry. As mentioned before, assay returns are often subjected to highly sophisticated statistical analysis.

Of extreme importance are the aspects of accident prevention and ventilation. Each mine has supervisors and staff personnel with strong specialties in both of these activities. As a result, it can be said that, in general, mining is by any statistical measurement as safe as most general construction work, and safer that some other occupations.

With regard to ventilation, the reader will be interested in knowing that mines handle a greater tonnage of ventilating air in a day than they do ore, the factor often reaching eight or so in a moderately deep mine. In one of the world's deepest mines, the factor is something like fourteen. It is the job of the ventilation engineer to maintain up-to-date surveys of the ventilation system, to ensure that the workings throughout the mine are being kept swept free of blasting fumes and dusts (Page 67).

Ore Trammed to Passes

The ore is drawn from the chutes of the different stopes on various working levels into ore cars and then hauled to the station where it is dumped down the main ore pass. This hauling or tramming as it is more commonly called is usually done by battery-driven, trolley, or diesel locomotives. Ore cars vary in capacity from one to ten tonnes. Nowadays, large tonnages are handled by diesel-driven load-haul-dump vehicles (Figures VII-9, VII-12).

An **ore pass** is the main channel into which the trammed ore is dumped and through which it flows to the underground crusher and loading pocket. From here it is hoisted to surface. This main channel is usually fed from each level by short branch raises as shown. Control chutes are usually established at various intervals in the ore pass system (Figure VII-1).

Common practice is to install a large jaw crusher at the bottom of the ore pass system just ahead of the loading pocket. This carries out the first or primary crushing. The reduced ore than enters a large chamber or bin from which it is fed to the skips.

Figure VII-15 — Cross-section of a typical open pit.

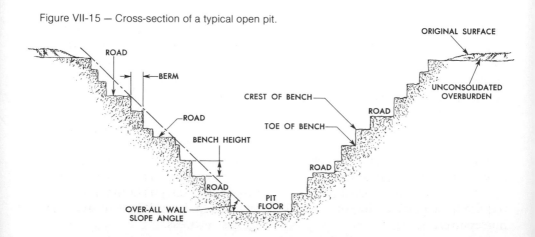

Figure VII-16 — Drag line operating at Fording Coal Ltd., Elkford, B.C.

Skips Carry Ore to Surface

The most common conveyance for carrying the ore to surface is the **skip.** These are self-dumping buckets and are usually operated in counterbalance in two separate shaft compartments to reduce the amount of power needed for hoisting. That is, the weight of the empty skip descending will tend to compensate for the weight of the other skip that is being hoisted.

Skips are of lightweight alloy construction and carry loads of around three to five tonnes per trip at speeds of the order of 300 meters per minute, for a modest sized operation. In larger operations, skips may have capacities of 12 tonnes or more, and travel at speeds up to 1,000 meters per minute. In such cases, and if the hoisting depth is 1,200 meters of so, the hoist will require to be powered by some 3,500 horsepower.

If the depths from which the ore is to be hoisted are not excessive, and if it is a tonnage proposition, hoisting by conveyor belts may be less costly. The conveyors travel upwards in a series of inclined ramps generally arranged to knuckle back after each conveyor travels its full length.

The skip dumps its load of ore into a bin in the mine headframe. From here it is conveyed by a system of rubber belts to the crusher house where it is further reduced in size by jaw crushers. In some few mines, the ore passes over a sorting belt, where barren rock that is readily visible as such is discarded, thus raising the overall grade of the ore that is fed to the mill.

From the jaw crusher the ore passes through a series of secondary crushers and screens before it is conveyed to the mill bins to start the recovery process.

Figure VII-17 — Hydraulic mining using water under high pressure to dislodge the coal is employed by Kaiser Resources at Sparwood, B.C. The coal is flumed out of the mine in slurry form and dewatered.

Figure VII-18 — For stripping rock covering coal seam, Kaiser Resources Ltd., Sparwood, B.C., uses this 25 cu. yd. shovel seen loading a 200-ton Lectrahaul truck.

When an orebody migrates a long distance from the main shaft due to dip tendencies or to faulting, it may be advisable to put down an underground shaft for further depth development. Such an underground shaft, which is offset from the main one, is called a **winze.** It may be a temporary expedient, or a permanent unit in which case it is more likely to approach the surface shaft in size. Level development will be handled from it in the usual way, although for a temporary unit, hoisting of ore would probably be in cars up the winze for **tramming** or transportation to the main ore pockets along the level.

In Canada, about 1,500 meters is the usual maximum vertical depth for a single-stage shaft. Such depths, of course, require very large hoisting units. Deepest single-stage shaft in the Western Hemisphere is the No. 9 shaft at Inco Limited's Creighton mine, near Sudbury, designed to lift ore from a depth of 2,180 meters.

Most new hoisting installations at large mines incorporate **friction-type hoists,** which enjoy lower operating costs.

At the bottom of any shaft or winze, a **sump** is provided for holding the water that develops in a mine so that it may be pumped either to surface or for use in the mine's water circuit. Shafts are divided into separate compartments, for skips, cages, manways, and service equipment such as water pipes, electric cables, etc. Leads for the latter are taken off at every level.

CHAPTER VIII

Recovering the Metals

Every successful new mine is presented, sooner or later, with the problem of erecting a mill or concentrator on its property. This represents the culmination of all the exploration and development work that has gone on before, assuming that the response to that work has been favorable. At the same time, it also presents problems, for it is at this stage that large amounts of money have to be provided to pay the heavy capital costs of construction and installation of mining and milling plant for continuous economic production.

A layman visiting a large mill or concentrator is impressed by a baffling maze of tanks, pipes, pumps, mills, conveyors, motors, chemicals, pulps, solutions — and noises. This seeming confusion is actually a carefully designed system with one objective — the recovery of valuable mineral in the form of a concentrate, or in the case of gold, the metal itself. It is the purpose of this chapter to explain something of the processes involved.

All milling and concentrating processes begin with crushing and grinding of the ore to suitable sizes, usually microscopic, and this operation accounts for the larger part of the process cost.

Separating Waste Minerals

Back in Chapter III the various principal ore minerals were described, as well as something of the ways in which they occur in the host rocks. It is now necessary to build upon that introduction by suggesting that ores are usually intimate mixtures of the valuable ore minerals interspersed within and among barren or worthless minerals which are referred to as **gangue.** If the reader will recall how granite looks when it is closely examined, he will have a sense of the sort of interlocking nature of the constituent minerals which make up that relatively coarse-grained rock.

Now if the scale is adjusted downward toward the microscopic we can think of much the same sort of mixture which may still be fairly simple, or which may have certain complications. For instance, in a complex sulphide ore we may have microscopic particles of say, sphalerite, existing as cores within small blebs of galena, or other sulphides. The purpose of crushing and grinding is to liberate these various constituents from each other as cleanly as possible, so that each may be recovered, or exposed to chemical action, by itself. The scale which is concerned here may be illustrated by introducing the term

mesh in which various testing sieves are calibrated. For example, a 200-mesh screen is constructed from wire cloth so fine that there are 200 openings per lineal inch or 79 per lineal centimeter. This works out to 6,200 openings per square centimeter, and each opening is 74 microns across; i.e. 74 thousandths of a millimeter. It is unusual in most ores to effect good liberation at sizes coarser than this.

At the same time, if the crushing and grinding part of the process is not controlled very carefully, a portion of sub-micron sizes is produced, and these may interfere with the subsequent operation. Thus, the objective is to reduce the ore in size through various closely controlled stages to that degree of fineness which gives an economic liberation of the valuable mineral, but which avoids as far as possible the production of sliming fractions. Hence, beginning with the underground crusher which is usually the primary, we have a system of machines, each of which is most efficient at a given size range, and each of which prepares the feed for the next stage of the size-reduction until the size of liberation is reached, usually in a ball mill.

Jaw Crushers Do First Work

After the ore is broken underground in the mine, it is hoisted to the surface and, usually, dumped into a coarse ore bin. Then it is fed to the first, or primary crusher. This is usually a jaw crusher which consists essentially of a fixed vertical jaw or plate, and a movable jaw at a slight vertical angle which is pushed backwards and forwards by a system of toggles. The rock falls into the opening between the jaws at the top and is crushed by the rapid, but short, forward movement of the movable jaw. The plates converge towards the bottom and thus the rock may be pinched and shattered several times before it falls free of the bottom opening.

Figure VIII-1 — Gyratory crusher used for second stage of crushing.

Frequently, the primary jaw crusher is installed underground at the bottom of the ore pass system. Thus, it is easier to load the skips if the larger chunks of ore are broken into smaller pieces.

The size of the jaw crusher is designated by the horizontal dimensions of the top opening. For example, a 38 cm x 61 cm crusher has an opening 38 cm wide and 61 cm long. It will take a piece of rock about 30 cm thick and reduce it to a minimum of 5 cm, at the rate of 25 tonnes per hour. It will require a 40 h.p. motor. Customary sizes of jaw crushers range from 23 cm x 38 cm for a small 50-tonne per day plant, up to 150 cm x 200 cm, and even larger. The machine is not highly efficient — few milling machines are. It is built either of steel plate, or of cast steel to withstand intense shocks. A pair of heavy flywheels are included to smooth out power requirements.

Secondary Crushing

A few large tonnage concentrators use a gyratory crusher for the primary breaker. It consists of a heavy gyratory crushing head mounted on a vertical shaft which works inside a crushing bowl fixed to the main frame. Rock falling into the bowl is caught and nipped by this gyrating head, falling through an opening of predetermined size. These crushers are made in sizes up to a capacity that can handle three or four thousand tonnes an hour; they are installed mainly on the surface at large mining properties.

The need of a secondary crusher frequently arises when the product from the primary crusher is too large for efficient grinding. In Canada the main type used is the Symons cone crusher, which for present purposes may be considered a cousin of the gyratory. However, its speed is greater, and it is designed to take a feed of ten to fifteen centimeters and reduce it to two centimeters or finer (Figure VIII-1).

Crushing is done dry and usually in a building separate from the mill or concentrator. Capacity is usually such that the entire tonnage requirement is crushed in one or two shifts. This allows balancing of power loads, and labor requirements, as well as allowing plenty of opportunity for repairs.

Size of the final product of the crusher house is usually controlled by a vibrating screen, the oversize from which is returned for further crushing. Belt conveyors move the ore between the various machines and to the fine ore bin.

Crusher houses are equipped with elaborate dust control and ventilation systems to eliminate the buildup of harmful dust particles in the air.

A mill or concentrator usually operates seven days a week and twenty-four hours a day, whereas the mine and crusher plant usually work only six days. Accordingly it is necessary to provide storage on the surface, and the customary place is immediately preceding the mill. These fine ore bins should contain at least thirty hours' requirements of crushed ore, and preferably more.

Ball Mill Grinds The Ore

Ore from these bins is fed, together with water, to one or more grinding units, consisting of a **ball mill** or rod mill, with or without a classifier (Figure VIII-2).

A ball mill consists essentially of a conical or cylindrical shell supported horizontally on hollow trunnion bearings on which it revolves. The ore enters through one trunnion opening and is discharged through the other. The mill is kept about one-half full of steel balls which, as the mill revolves, cascade and roll over each other to crush and grind the ore between them. Size of balls varies from 2 cm to 13 cm, depending on the size of the feed and toughness of the ore. Naturally as the balls wear smaller they form a graduated size and only the largest size is added to maintain the ball charge.

A **rod mill** differs from a ball mill mainly by using steel rods instead of balls. These rods are from five cm to 10 cm in diameter and are approximately the length of the grinding mill (Figure VIII-3).

A grinding mill usually is not smaller than 1.5 m in diameter and may range up to 3.75 m. Power required customarily ranges from 50 to 300 horsepower. But larger mills are used. At Cominco's Sullivan concentrator a 3.5 m diameter x 3.75 m long rod mill is used for coarse grinding. It is driven by a 950 horsepower motor. The ball mills are five 3 m x 1.25 m Hardinge mills, each requiring 250 horsepower.

There has been a growing trend throughout the world to use some form of **autogenous grinding.**

New plants are being built using some variety of this form of pulverizing and existing plants are converting parts of their grinding systems to pebble grinding, replacing steel rods and balls. Ore can be made to crush and grind itself (autogenously) in either wet or dry grinding mills. The wet grinding plants can be divided into three divisions:—

(1) Primary autogenous grinding, in which run of mine ore with pieces up to 45 cm in size are fed into large diameter (up to 7-meter) mills and ground to final milling size in one step.

(2) Secondary autogenous grinding or semi-autogenous grinding or rock pebble milling, in which fine grinding

Figure VIII-2 — Ball mill operating in closed circuit with Akins classifier.

Figure VIII-3 — Rod mill at Thompson mine, Northern Manitoba, with control panel in background.

is done in conventional sized mills equipped with fast discharge grates after the ore has been crushed to at least 2 cm in size. There may be several stages of pebble mills with different sized media in each stage. The pebbles are obtained by screening suitable sizes from the jaw crusher discharge.

(3)   Combination processes in which the first stage is crushing and grinding in a primary autogenous mill, removing rounded ore pebbles from this mill for use in a secondary fast discharge pebble mill in which the fine grinding is continued down to the final desired mesh.

Autogenous grinding has become very popular in Canada, and large tonnages are ground each day in autogenous mills of one kind or another.

It is natural to expect that there will be considerable variation in the size of particles discharged from the grinding mill. Some will be too coarse, some just the right size, and some finer than needed. The coarser particles should be separated from the balance of the material for efficiency of the subsequent treatment.

It is the function of the **classifier** to perform a separation and return the oversize particles to the grinding mills for further grinding.

A classifier often consists of a box set on a slope of about one in four and containing a mechanism for moving material up the incline. This mechanism may consist of a series of reciprocating rakes or paddles, as in the Dorr classifier, or a slowly revolving spiral as in the Akins classifier. Other kinds of classifiers have come into wide use in newer plants; these frequently operate on a centrifugal principle, somewhat similar to the cyclone dust collector.

In operation of the Dorr or Akins classifier, the pulp discharged from the grinding mill flows down a **launder** to the classifier, entering the bottom end of the inclined tank which forms a pool. Here the heavier coarser particles settle to the bottom of the tank and are caught by the rakes or spiral and moved upwards to the top end of the tank. From here they flow by gravity into the feed end of the grinding mill. Meanwhile the finer particles do not settle, but are carried by a current of controlled velocity over an adjustable weir at the bottom end of the tank as finished particles.

When a ball mill and classifier work together as a unit it is termed grinding in **closed circuit** (Figure VIII-2). The ground ore so produced will have a certain maximum size, with amount of finest size controlled to some extent. Usually a ball mill grinds in closed circuit for maximum control and efficiency.

A rod mill may be used to prepare feed for a ball mill, in which case it may operate without a classifier, or as it is termed, in **open circuit.** By the nature of its grinding medium, a rod mill has a series of line contacts

with the ore particles, rather than point contacts as in a ball mill. Accordingly a rod mill should produce less oversize than ball mill, and thus, in certain functions may not require a classifier.

Figure VIII-4 — Operators tend flotation machines at United Keno Hill mine in Yukon.

The Ore Is Ground

Again, the crushing and grinding part of the process has the function of reducing the ore in size through successive stages, until the best possible liberation has been attained, consistent with expense. The product becomes the feed to the recovery process, whether it be in a cyanidation mill for the winning of metallic gold, or a flotation plant in which metallic sulphides are separated from the bulk of the worthless gangue materials and sometimes from each other. We shall now consider some of these processes, beginning with the recovery of gold by treating its ores with cyanide, as this still constitutes an interesting part of Canadian mineral activity.

The search for gold has resulted in modern towns frequently hundreds of miles from the nearest road or railroad. In the case of gold mining, there is the unique advantage that the product of months of work will be represented by a few bars of bullion that can be easily transported by airplane over miles of bush country.

Throughout the centuries gold has been recovered in many ways, from the Golden Fleece of the ancient Argonauts, the rocker or long tom of the California Forty-niner, and the noisy stamp mill of the nineteenth century. However, the gold production of Canada today is mainly obtained by the use of the cyanide process.

Milling methods for the treatment of gold ores must study and take advantage of the natural characteristics of the metal. Gold occurs as the native metal, and as such differs from copper (excepting the native copper of Michigan), lead, zinc, nickel and the other so-called base metals. By **native gold** is

Figure VIII-5 — Ten giant grinding mills at Inco's Clarabelle mill at Sudbury produce the pulp for the flotation section. Five ball mills are at the near end of the line followed by five rod mills at the far end which do the first stage grinding.

Figure VIII-6 — The control room, a feature of all modern mills, which monitors the crushing, grinding, flotation and other operations.

meant the naturally occurring element which has the familiar color we all know in gold rings. Gold usually has a varying amount of silver with it, and rarely some **tellurides.**

Dissolving the Gold

Gold can be dissolved by very few chemicals, one of which is **cyanide.** This chemical is white in appearance, very poisonous, and dissolves easily in water. Many readers will recognize it as the base of various rodent poisons. It does have the property when in solution, and in the presence of oxygen, of slowly attacking fine particles of gold and ultimately dissolving them. Peculiarly, and happily, a weak cyanide solution attacks the gold particles faster than a strong solution. Necessary to the chemistry of this is the presence of oxygen, obtained from the air.

For the cyanide to attack the gold particles it is necessary that the gold be liberated from the worthless gangue rock with which it is surrounded. Cyanide will not attack or dissolve this enveloping rock. To liberate the tiny particle is an expensive problem.

The mathematically minded are asked to consider for a moment that a gold ore containing only six or seven grams of gold per ton of rock can be profitably treated. With gold at around six or seven dollars per gram, this means that not much more than a few grams of gold must be found and liberated in a ton of rock. And when one considers that a modern cyanide mill recovers or extracts 95 to 98% of the gold in the ore, the efficiency of the process is appreciated.

In a cyanide mill, lime and cyanide are added to the grinding circuit. The lime has various functions, one being to protect the cyanide from being destroyed by some natural occurring chemicals called cyanicides, another to improve settlement of the pulp in the thickeners as later described.

In the **cyanidation process,** it is natural to expect that dissolving of

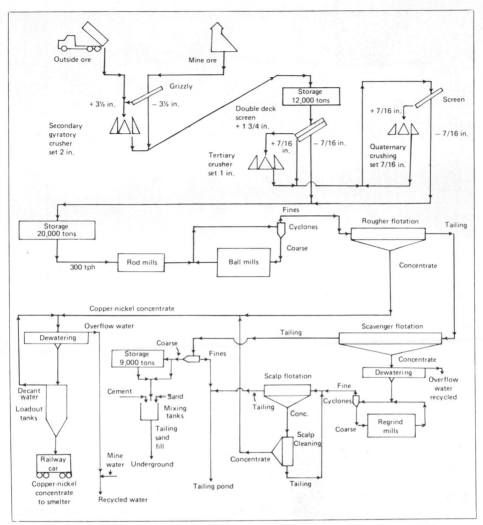

Figure VIII-7 — A flow sheet for treating a base metal ore. This is the 8,500-ton daily capacity Strathcona mill in the Sudbury area, Northern Ontario. It produces a bulk nickel-copper concentrate as a slurry which is shipped in tank cars to the Falconbridge smelter, 64 km away.

the gold will begin in the grinding circuit. The conditions are ideal — fresh solutions have been introduced, newly liberated gold particles are constantly being polished by the grinding action, and the solutions are warmed by the energy liberated by the grinding. Depending on the ore and fineness of grind, from 30 to 70% of gold may be dissolved during the grinding period.

Additional time is the only requirement of placing the balance of the liberated gold in solution. Accordingly the gold-bearing pulp is pumped to a number of mixing tanks, termed **agitators.** Here the **pulp** is aerated either mechanically, or by compressed air, or by a combination of both, for a predetermined length of time. This varies anywhere from 24 to 48 hours.

Figure VIII-8 — Pulp is introduced into the centre of the tanks for thickening, heavy solids sink to the bottom and are moved to the outlet by slowly moving rakes, while clear solution at the surface overflows to a launder at the inside rim of the tank.

Separate Worthless Rock

The first part of the extraction process has now been completed — dissolving the gold in the cyanide solution. Then it becomes necessary to separate the valuable solution from the now worthless finely ground rock.

The next step, therefore, is to move the pulp from the agitators to one or more **thickeners.** These latter machines, as all other machines described, operate continuously. They are large diameter, comparatively shallow, round tanks. As the feed enters, the finely ground rock particles sink to the bottom, are slowly raked to the centre by mechanical arms, and discharged through a cone connected to a pipe in the bottom.

Some of the extremely fine particles are aided in settling by the lime, previously mentioned, which seems to make them coalesce. The solution overflows the top of the tanks, and is collected in a **launder** around the outside.

Movement of all mechanism is comparatively slow to allow an undisturbed settlement. Thickeners are usually 9 meters to 15 meters in diameter and 3.5 to 4.5 meters deep. Larger sizes are used in warmer climates, where it is not necessary to house them from the weather.

Horizontal trays are sometimes installed to divide the thickener into compartments, each of which operates individually, thus increasing the capacity of the thickener. The pulp as discharged from the bottom of the thickener is quite thick, but still contains too much valuable material to be discarded. Accordingly it is filtered.

A **filter** is simply a large drum, 2.5 meters to 3.0 meters in diameter, and 3.0 meters to 4.5 meters long, slowly rotating on a horizontal shaft. The drum is porous and partially submerged in a semi-circular steel tank, into which pulp from the bottom of the thickener is pumped (Figure VIII-9).

Filtering Removes Valuable Solution

As the drum rotates, a vacuum is applied from within which causes a definite thickness of pulp to adhere to the drum. Further vacuum then sucks out the solution. Water is sprayed onto the outside top of the rotating drum to wash out any entrapped solution. This the vacuum also catches. Some mills filter twice to be sure all the valuable solution is caught. Then the filter cake drops into a box, is mixed with water, and pumped to the tailing pond. It is now the final reject, or **tailing,** from the mill and resembles soupy clay in appearance. Gradually it fills the pond into which it is pumped, dries and hardens. Formerly, tailings were pumped into swamp areas, or small lakes, but modern practice requires that they be adequately contained so that they cannot drain into the surrounding countryside. Dams or other barriers may be erected to contain the tailings which eventually build into huge piles or mounds which are chemically treated so that they can support trees and other vegetation.

Figure VIII-9 — Drum filters used in the milling process for separating solutions from the finely ground ore, and for reducing the moisture content of mineral concentrates.

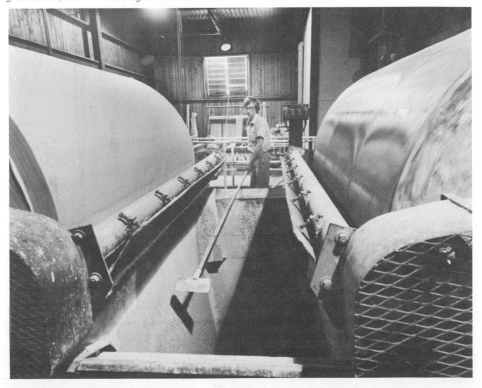

All the gold is now contained in solutions from the thickener overflow and the filter. These are collected in a tank and then pumped through canvas sheets to remove any fine clay particles. This process is called **clarification.** The treated solutions are sparkling clear, with a light green tint. The gold bearing solutions are then passed through a precipitation process, which consists mainly of adding fine zinc dust. This combines with the gold in the solution and forms a **precipitate** which is caught between leaves of canvas in a filter press, from which it is removed usually at 10-day intervals.

This gold precipitate is quite impure, and looks like black mud, having iron, zinc, some copper and a variety of other contaminants mixed with it. Refining is the next and final treatment.

Refine Precipitate

The most spectacular part of the entire process now occurs. Silica, borax and soda ash are added to the dried precipitate, which is heated in an oil-fired, oval shaped, tilting furnace. This results in a miniature smelting operation. On the top of the melt is the slag containing the impurities, while the molten gold, on account of its greater weight, sinks to the bottom.

The furnace is fired by oil, which is blown in by compressed air. When the charge is completely fluid, the furnace is tilted and the molten contents poured into a conical mold. Black slag forms on the top, which is broken from the underlying gold button when cool. The button or buttons (there may be enough

precipitate to necessitate more than one melt) are again placed in the furnace, melted and poured into bar molds. The sight of the molten gold flowing from the furnace is never forgotten by those who have witnessed it.

Finally the bars are weighed, alternate corners drilled for samples to determine purity (expressed as fineness in parts per thousand) and packed for shipping. In due course the mine receives a cheque for the gold, while the gold itself, after further refining, goes forth to be used in the arts or industry, or to serve as backing for the world's currencies.

Treatment of Base Metals

Base metals require a more complex treatment before assuming their ultimate commercial form. In this country they are usually found associated with sulphur, in a crystal form known as sulphides. So we have copper occurring with varying amounts of sulphur, and/or iron, to form minerals with various names and chemical compositions.

The economics of base metal treatment differs from gold as it is not usual to produce the practically finished metal at the mine. This is due to the fact that a mine is usually not sufficiently large and fortunately situated to warrant by itself the huge and complex interlocking of concentrator, refinery and rolling mills or fabricating plants.

Instead each base metal mine attempts to remove locally as much of the waste rock as possible from its ore, and ship the enriched product to a strategically located smelter or other reduction works.

This process of removing the waste rock and separating the valuable sulphides of the metals is termed **concentrating.** The mill is a **concentrator,** and the product, as may be expected, is a **concentrate.**

Reasons for Concentrating

Assuming a copper property has a grade of one and one half per cent copper, and is treating 2,000 tonnes of ore a day, it can theoretically produce the equivalent of 30 tonnes of copper metal a day. However, the copper in the ore occurs as a copper sulphide, and the concentrate so produced may only contain 20% copper. So theoretically, we may have 100 divided by 20 multiplied by 30 equalling approximately 150 tonnes of concentrate a day. Actually no process is perfect, and so we may obtain only 140 tonnes.

However, it can be realized that a concentrator of the above size would probably require a railroad for hauling away this material, as well as bringing in required supplies. Thus it differs from a gold mine, where a month's production is represented by a few bars easily carried by a small airplane.

It should be further realized that a 2,000 tonne capacity copper concentrator is comparatively small. Many are of 5,000 tonnes, while Utah Copper in the United States has a rated capacity of 100,000 tonnes every 24 hours. Thus it becomes really a complex industrial enterprise of railroads, housing, schools, power development, hoisting, crushing, grinding, etc., and, of paramount importance, labor relationship.

The concentrate is shipped smelter, whereby a heat treat in combination with various chemicals produces an impure copper metal called **blister co** This product is then treated in refinery to obtain the commerc pure metal. But the refinery ma located many miles from the smelter, the location being chose where electric power is cheap. A fabricating plant completes the picture.

The purpose of the concentrator is to remove and discard the waste rock from the valuable minerals. Thus, the capacity of the smelter ca be utilized to produce a maximum amount of metal. Also, it will be realized that a great saving in freight will result from hauling 140 tonnes of concentrate instead of 2,000 tonnes of ore.

Crushing and grinding in a concentrator are practised in the same manner as in a cyanide mill, and for the same purpose, i.e., to release the valuable mineral from the surrounding worthless rock.

Sulphides are Floated

Grinding of base metal ores is done in water to which certain oils and synthetic chemicals are added. Then the resulting **pulp** (finely ground rock in water) is swirled around in rectangular tanks in series, known as flotation machines. Controlled air and further chemicals, called flotation reagents, are added. The air forms bubbles in the pulp, the flotation reagents coat the sulphides — and not the waste particles — and cause them to stick to the bubbles which in turn merrily carry the

sulphides to the top of the tanks; much in the manner of the old-time free balloon ascensions (Fig. VIII-4).

The sulphide-carrying bubbles are scraped mechanically from the top of the flotation machines. Meanwhile the worthless rock sinks to the bottom of the machine and is discharged to waste.

Specific gravity has nothing to do with the separation, as the sulphides that are carried up by the bubbles are heavier than the unattached minerals that sink. Call it black art if you wish — its technical name is **flotation.** Actually nobody yet knows exactly what happens, in spite of hundreds of books of theoretical dissertations (Figure VIII-4).

Later the mineral-bearing bubbles, now known as a concentrate, have the water removed before shipment. Sometimes mechanical drying is carried out to reduce weight if the distance to be shipped is great.

By employing various flotation reagents, different kinds of sulphides can be floated or separated one at a time. For example, suppose an ore contains copper-zinc, and iron sulphides. It is possible to make three separate concentrates, one containing the copper sulphides, another the zinc, and a third the iron, although most likely the iron sulphides will be discarded as waste. Similarly in a lead-zinc ore, the lead sulphides and the zinc sulphides can be recovered as separate concentrates. This selective flotation of lead-zinc ores has been of great economic importance, and made possible the profitable operation of the great Sullivan Mine at Kimberley, British Columbia.

Flotation is occasionally applied to gold ores, to make a gold flotation concentrate which is then cyanided, with or without roasting. This method is especially applicable when the metal is very fine and intimately associated with sulphide or arsenide minerals. In this manner it is possible to make say ten tonnes of gold concentrate from 300 tonnes of mill feed. This concentrate can be economically treated much more intensely (finer grinding and longer agitation) than the original ore.

Heavy-Media Separation

Another method of concentrating ores and minerals by floating — but actually quite different from the flotation method described above — is that known as the **heavy-media separating process.** More commonly called the **sink-float process,** it employs the differences in specific gravity of the various rocks and minerals to effect separation.

In the sink-float plant, coarsely crushed ore is fed into a suspension of finely-ground ferrosilicon or magnetite, or other heavy mineral, in water. This suspension is carefully maintained at a specific gravity between that of the desired feed and the unwanted minerals or gangue. Thus the heavier mineral components sink, while the lighter constituents float.

Some plants use this process without further beneficiation, examples of which are to be found in the iron ore, coal and gravel industries.

Leaching Holds Much Promise

Like other branches of the mining

industry, there is an ever constant struggle to mill ores and recover minerals and metals more efficiently and more cheaply. In this connection, mention must be made of **leaching,** a comparative newcomer to the milling industry. It is a process that is used for the recovery of uranium as well as a host of other base and precious metals.

One of the leading pioneers in this field has been Sherritt Gordon Mines Ltd., which company, after years of research, developed a new leaching process for producing nickel, copper and cobalt from concentrates from its Lynn Lake mine in Northern Manitoba. This employs an ammonia pressure leach, sometimes known as the Forward process after its discoverer, F. A. Forward. The process is used at the Sherritt Gordon plant at Fort Saskatchewan, Alberta, where nickel, copper and cobalt are recovered.

In Sherritt's case, the nickel and copper are concentrated separately

Figure VIII-10 — The ion exchange section where uranium is extracted at Denison Mines, Elliot Lake, Ontario.

at the mine (these concentrates grade approximately 12% nickel and 29% copper, respectively). The sulphide concentrates are then shipped to the leaching plant, where the leaching takes place with ammonia under compressed air. Both the nickel and the copper, together with a small cobalt content, are dissolved and subsequently separated and recovered. The sulphur is converted to ammonium sulphate, which is recovered as a byproduct and used in the fertilizer industry.

A somewhat different adaption of the leaching process, employing an acid leach (sulphuric acid), is used in the uranium mills in Northern Saskatchewan and the Elliot Lake area of Ontario.

These processes are coming into wider use both for base metal and uranium ores (under the term of **hydrometallurgy**). While revolutionary as to techniques, they are not unlike the cyanidation process which we have described in some detail. Acutally, cyanidation is a form of leaching. But these later leaching plants are both complex and more costly to construct.

Magnetic separation is a beneficiation process which is now widely used in the treatment of low grade iron ore; in fact it has made possible the mining and treatment of vast amounts of material in Canada that not long ago were considered worthless.

All iron minerals are susceptible magnetically in at least some degree, with magnetite the highest of all; the list also includes various hematites lower down in the scale. In the process, the crude ore, which may grade less than 30% in iron, is ground in water to a suitable fineness in a mill with classification control. The pulp is then passed over a revolving magnetic drum, to which the magnetic particles are attracted and from which they are scraped at a convenient quadrant in the rotation, as the gangue particles pass along to waste.

The magnetic portion is unwatered and filtered. As the concentrate is too fine in size to be used in a blast furnace at the customer's steel plant, it is **pelletized** by mixing with a suitable bonding agent and rolled in a large pan, or within a drum, until the particles are agglomerated into small balls a centimeter or so in diameter. These pellets are dried and baked. Such is the effect of this process that iron ore pellets, grading in some cases better than 60% iron, are considered as first class feed to the blast furnace, and enjoy premium prices (Figure VIII-11).

Asbestos Milling

The milling of asbestos is accomplished as a dry operation to separate the asbestos fibres from the mine rock. The veins of longer fibres, which are especially valuable, are sorted out by hand, a process known as **cobbing.**

The milling procedure is designed to preserve the length of the fibres, but at the same time to open them as much as possible and to keep the entrapped grist and dust to a minimum. The basic operations include crushing, drying, fibre separation and grading. Shaking screens and air suction **(aspiration)** are used to separate the fibres, while

Figure VIII-11 — Iron ore pellets come off travelling grate machine after being hardened at temperature of over 1,300°C.

impact mills serve to fiberize or fluff out the fibres.

As might be expected, elaborate dust control measures are installed to prevent the escape of minute fibre particles into the atmosphere in order to meet stringent control measures required by government regulation.

Microbiological Leaching

For many centuries, even from Roman times, the action of water-entrained oxygen on metallic sulphides has been recognized and used, particularly with regard to copper-iron minerals. This results in the breaking down of the sulphide minerals and the generation of weak sulphuric and sulphurous acids, which take the metal into solution as sulphates and sulphites, often leaving a precipitate of ferric iron. The process has been used deliberately, and mainly to recover copper from mine drainage waters, and from surface waters percolating through old mine dumps and waste heaps, by precipitating the acidic solutions on scrap iron.

Only in recent years it has become known that the rate of the action is heavily dependent upon the presence of certain bacterial micro-organisms, who derive their life energy not from carbonaceous foods, but rather from the oxidation of sulphur and various metals. The phenomena has given rise to an active field of research, and is producing economic benefits in the heap leaching of low grade copper ores which are cheaply mined in open pits, particularly in the southwestern United States.

Leach Uranium

Other metals have also been leached successfully in laboratory experiments, and in Ontario some uranium oxide is being cheaply recovered from old worked out stopes.

The process, and the little organisms which play such a large part in it and which work without pay, are the basis of **solution mining** employed at Agnew Lake as previously mentioned.

Smelting

The concentrates from the flotation, or other physical beneficiation processes, are shipped to a plant known as a **smelter** for the actual recovery of the contained metals from the sulphides, oxides, antimonides, arsenides, etc., of the ore minerals themselves. We have already referred to the wet leaching process used by Sherritt Gordon at Fort Saskatchewan, Alberta, which is used to treat a complex nickel-copper sulphide concentrate, but the term **smelting** as we shall view it here is applied to reduction processes carried out in the dry state at incandescent temperatures.

With the exception of gold, platinum, some silver, and minor amounts of copper, all metals used by man exist in nature in what chemists refer to as the **oxidized** state. This includes all combinations in which the metal is linked chemically to non-metallic elements and compounds, such as sulphur, sulphates, and a wide variety of others. The converse of oxidation is **reduction,** and this refers to the removal of the chemical link between the metal and the oxidizing elements and compounds, and the gathering of the metal as it becomes isolated from those oxidizing impurities. This is what is accomplished in all smelters, hydrometallurgical works, and refineries, though the actual processes may differ sharply, and even widely, among them.

Perhaps the least complicated non-ferrous smelter is one which treats copper sulphide ores for the production of **blister copper,** which will most likely be further refined electrolytically before entering manufacture. Thus, we shall follow the processes of such a smelter, beginning with the receipt of copper concentrates in the yard. For convenience, let us assume that the concentrate will have a grade of about 26% in copper, linked with iron and sulphur in the form of the ore mineral, chalcopyrite

The first operation will consist of **roasting,** and in the specialized machine, the roaster, the concentrate is heated to high temperatures and kept in contact with oxygen in the form of air, or oxygen-enriched air.

This has the effect of burning off a part of the sulphur, but, more important is its function of changing the copper-iron-sulphur complexes to chemical forms which are more amenable to the smelting or reduction process proper. In roasting, part of the sulphur actually acts as a fuel, and in some roasters little or no additional fuel need be added once the system has been brought to incandescence. The product of the roaster is known as a **calcine,** and in our example its grade in copper has been increased to perhaps 31%.

The calcine is mixed with various reagents known as **fluxes** whose composition will be suited to the gangue minerals of the ore, as for instance silica for an ore high in lime, and vice versa. The mixture is fed to a **reverberatory furnace.** This furnace is essentially a long, flat chamber, equipped with a heating mechanism at one end from which a hot flame is shot the length of the furnace, and a flue system at the other for the removal of the hot gases. In it, two functions are carried out. In the first place, we have the reaction between the fluxes and the gangue minerals of the ore with the formation of various low-melting silicates or **slags.** Secondly, there is

Figure VIII-12 — Converter aisle at Inco's Thompson smelter.

the formation of a **matte** which contains the copper, and most of the iron, both in chemical combination with the sulphur, but which also gathers and dissolves any precious metals which may be present. In the furnace, which incidentally operates at temperatures above 1,100°C, the slag floats on top of the heavier matte and is tapped off periodically to be sent to the dump, presenting a spectacular scene at night.

The molten matte, now grading about 46% in copper, is also tapped off and poured into a **converter** (Figure VIII-12), together with more fluxes and reducing agents, and is blown with air. In this final furnace treatment, the iron becomes fully oxidized and unites with the fluxes to form a slag. The copper becomes reduced to its elemental state, and the last of the sulphur is driven off in the form of sulphur dioxide. Again, as in the reverberatory furnace, the slag floats on top of the molten mass, and is periodically decanted off for return to the reverb, as it contains some copper.

The molten copper, now about 99% pure, is known as **blister,** and after a further slight fire-refining, is cast into shapes known as **anodes.** These are shipped to an electrolytic refinery for the purification of the copper to commercial specifications, and for the recovery of the precious metals which the copper has gathered to itself in the converter.

In the electrolytic plant, the copper anodes are placed in tanks containing an **electrolyte** of dissolved copper sulphate. Thin sheets of pure copper are also placed in the tanks to act as **cathodes.**

Electric current is passed through the system of anode-electrolyte-cathode, and the copper is carried from the anodes to build up on the cathodes in a highly purified form. Eventually, the cathodes are removed and melted down for casting into various commercial shapes, of which the most important are **wirebars.** Any precious metals in the copper anodes fall to the bottom of the tank with the last of the impurities and become contained in a muddy deposit, whence they are recovered and refined in a separate process (Figure VIII-13).

The smelting of complex nickel-copper sulphide ore, and the refining of their contained metals, embraces a much more complicated suite of processes, but do however follow the general ideas outlined above for the smelting of copper.

At Trail, B.C., Canada has a large plant for the reduction of lead from sulphide concentrates. In this plant, the concentrate is roasted in a **sintering machine,** and then fed to a **blast furnace** along with coke, which acts as a fuel and as a reducing agent, and various fluxes. The actual reduction to metallic lead is carried out entirely in this furnace, which produces an impure lead bullion. The bullion is refined electrolytically, and the precious metals contained are recovered in much the same way as in the case of copper refining, as has been indicated.

The treatment of zinc concentrates follows a pattern of roasting to a form such that all of the sulphur has been driven off, and the resulting calcine consists of zinc

Figure VIII-13 — Copper anodes for refining into pure copper.

oxides and sulphates, iron oxides and sulphates, and the various gangue minerals. The calcine is leached with sulphuric acid for the dissolution of the oxides in the form of sulphates. The leach solution is purified chemically so that a pure zinc sulphate solution may be fed to an electrolytic tank for its final reduction to the pure metal.

Production Means Heavy Expenditures

Why does a mill or concentrator cost so much? Of course the equipment is expensive, and it must be installed in a building on substantial concrete foundation, together with auxiliary equipment such as pumps, conveyors, pipe lines for heat, water and solutions, starting switches, lights, etc. Modern practice favors fireproof construction if such materials are reasonbly available. Mills designed in these days are very sophisticated with regard to their control systems. Samples are taken from many points during the process, and assay returns given almost immediately to a computer

Figure VIII-14 — Skimming molten zinc which has just been poured into molds in continuous casting machine at Texasgulf operation, Timmins, Ontario. The horn-like device is a fan for cooling.

feed-back system which adjusts amounts of reagents fed, densities of pulps, etc.

A rough rule of thumb for a flotation concentrator and ancillary surface buildings suggests a cost of several thousands of dollars per daily tonne of capacity. Costs will vary widely according to location, degree of automation, etc.

When a decision is reached to bring a property into production, there are a number of heavy expenditures entailed, in addition to the cost of the mill itself. For instance, a heavier or a new electric power line may be necessary, with a new substation and switches. To maintain continuous production, a larger hoist than that used for shaft sinking, will probably be required, together with compressors, a water supply system, a change house for the men and perhaps a new head frame. Shops are needed for maintenance and repair work. A permanent staff must be hired, which frequently means houses, a school, hospital, a sewage system, roads, etc. In recent years, measures to guard against pollution and to protect the environment have added substantially to plant costs.

CHAPTER IX

Protecting the Environment

Nearly 3,000 years ago, it was written in Proverbs 14:4, "Where no oxen are, the stable is clean, but much increase is by the strength of the ox."

The writer of that quotation had his finger squarely on an aspect of industrial concern which exercises all of us today. All industrial activity — even including agriculture — produces at least some upset in the ecology. We are still far from knowing the extent to which levels in various sorts of pollution are harmful to man and other animals, and in what ways. We know pretty well what the pollutants are, how they are formed, and their chemical and physical properties have been in the books for many years. We are still less sure about the physiological extent of the harm they do, and the optimum level of concentration which should not be exceeded. Against this, there is a strong economic aspect, and balances need to be found between the costs of correction and the loss involved in industrial activity.

In the mining world, the greatest chemical fact of the matter is that almost all of our metals are extracted from sulphide ores, which in most cases contain iron, and in the present context iron may be considered as a reactive metal as we shall discuss.

Sulphur in its most common forms, sulphuric acid and sulphates, affects groundwater and streams, and as sulphur dioxide it is a constituent of the atmosphere.

Atmospheric sulphur dioxide comes from other sources besides human activity. Volcanic action contributes at least as much as industry in each year, and it has been estimated that the eruption of Krakatao in 1883 put into the earth's atmosphere as much sulphur as has man in his entire industrial history. Hence, it is estimated that only about six per cent of the atmosphere's sulphur dioxide is the result of smelting and other industrial activity. These activities, however, are carried on where people live, are therefore very visible, and properly matters of concern.

There are other pollutants as well, such as dusts produced from many industrial substances and in many ways; these are often hygenically hazardous, and in any case have unsightly and inconvenient effects. Finely divided particles settle but slowly in water, and may impart turbidity to a stream or lake for several kilometers. Industrial noise has also become recognized as a form of pollution.

In all, mining and smelting operations in Canada disturb about 65,000 hectares of land, including open pit mines and tailings disposal areas, scattered among about 200 mining operations, many of which are in remote locations.

Let us now consider in some little detail the sources of various kinds of environmental disturbance that are of concern here, and for convenience we shall list them by the various sectors of the industry.

Metal Mining, Milling and Smelting

We are involved here with two principal sources: firstly, the waters which find their ways into the groundwater environment from mine drainage, mill effluents in tailings, and process waters from refinery operations; and secondly, the stack gases from smelters and pyrometallurgical works.

We have already referred to the common occurrence of base metal ores as natural compounds of the sought-after metal with iron and sulphur. In addition to these, and fortunately quite rare and local in our present context, are various arsenides, antimonides, etc.

In the presence of water and its dissolved oxygen, such iron-sulphur-base metal ores undergo certain natural processes at normal temperatures and pressures, generating various soluble compounds which find their way into the hydrosphere. These are not highly concentrated, but contain enough acid and salts of heavy metals to be harmful and often result in unsightly effects. Taking, for instance, the action of oxygen-containing water on one of the iron sulphides, we have a series or group of reactions which goes on quite spontaneously. Some of the reactions are intermediate or momentary, but they produce in turn various iron sulphates, perhaps some elemental sulphur, and sulphuric acid. These alone are potential contaminants, even in the weak concentrations characteristic of a fairly free-flowing hydrosphere and even considering the slow speed at which the chemical reactions take place at ordinary temperatures. As mentioned earlier in another context, the reactions are hastened by the presence of certain rather ubiquitous bacteria, and it is estimated that these can affect the speed of the process by a factor as much as five.

In turn, and taking as an example the copper sulphide portion of the mineral chalcopyrite, it is attacked by the iron sulphates which have been generated as above, and by the sulphuric acid in this chemically acid environment, to form soluble copper sulphate, and the generation of still more acid. The production of "cement copper" is simply the reversal of this, and is effected by precipitating the copper on metallic iron. Any high school chemistry text will show the various reactions which take place. Other so-called heavy metals are dissolved in the same way, and when we think about it, this sort of chemistry provides the basis for geochemical prospecting.

All mines receive surface waters down to depths of 200 meters or so, as well as waters supplied for drilling, dust suppression, and human needs. It is therefore common for the drainage waters of metal mines to be slightly acid, and to carry sulphates of iron and other metals. It is most common for mines to neutralize their drainage water with lime before pumping it to surface, in order to protect the pumps and piping. Often this water is sufficiently innocuous to be used in the various milling processes which are usually carried out in slightly alkaline conditions.

Another way in which the chemistry described above concerns us lies in the tailings which are delivered from the mill or concentrator and which are impounded in areas selected for the purpose. The solutions contained in the tailings and the surface waters which percolate through them require to be neutralized before they mingle with the natural drainage of the region.

Within the milling process, large quantities of water are used, perhaps several hundreds of litres per minute per daily tonne of capacity. This water contains small concentrations of various reagents. The industry has long been aware of this particular kind of disturbance to the environment, and, typically, at one large operation the mill water demand of 60 million litres per day is now made up of about 45 million litres of recirculating water.

In refinery processes, a great deal of water is used, in gas scrubbers, purification cycles of electrolytes, and here again much care is taken to make sure that the amounts of heavy metals reaching the earth's waters are innocuous.

All coals contain some iron sulphides, and the same chemistry applies. In the United States the attendant problems are quite severe, but in Canada they seem to be less so. In eastern Canada mine drainage water, after neutralization, is usually pumped to the ocean. In western Canada, the coals occur in the alkaline environment of limestones, and so there is a built-in neutralizing effect.

The effluents of gold mines are not too bad. It has been explained that gold is extracted from its ores by applying very weak solutions of sodium cyanide in slightly alkaline conditions, with regeneration and re-circulation of the cyanide after final precipitation of the gold. The slight traces of cyanide in effluents are quickly rendered into relatively innocuous compounds in the slightest acidic environment.

One contaminant of the environment is windblown dust from the older and inactive portions of tailings impoundment areas. As far back as fifty years, gold mines in Porcupine and Kirkland Lake, for instance, converted their relatively small lake-filled dumps into parks, by applying topsoil and planting grass. This kind of effort has been intensified in recent years, and many mines have addressed themselves to this problem. In one recent year alone, some twenty mines had reclaimed 600 of 1,400 hectares of old disposal areas by treating their surfaces in such ways that vegetation in the form of selected species, and even small trees, could thrive, thus preventing the blowing of dusts, and making them generally agreeable from an aesthetic standpoint. Other mining concerns have followed suit, so that now almost all but the

Figure IX-1 — A crop of grain is grown on mill tailings at uranium mine at Elliot Lake, Ontario.

currently active, water-covered portions of tailings ponds have been at least partially treated.

A great deal of attention is also being applied to the construction of the dams which are built to confine the tailings to a particular area, and also for their proper operation.

With regard to the groundwater problem, in summary, it seems that the most practicable measures used thus far have included neutralizing with lime, which is a relatively inexpensive alkali. Considerable research continues in governmental and other agencies, directed to the finding of other means. These include neutralizing with limestone aggregate, the flocculation of particulates, the addition of bacteriophages to slow down the chemistry we have referred to, and such exotic measures as "reverse osmosis", and ion exchange.

Smelter Gases and Dusts

We have come a long way since the turn of the century when a crude process known as "heap roasting" was used to treat some sulphide ores in the open air, allowing large volumes of sulphur dioxide to affect the vegetation of hundreds of square kilometers of area. The process was discarded many years ago, and the areas referred to have pretty well recovered from the effects.

The sulphur input to a smelter, which is contained in the sulphide ores it treats, is large, in the order of several hundreds of tonnes per day. Beginning about fifty years ago, Canadian smelters of base metal ores installed plants for the recovery of sulphur dioxide, and for its conversion to sulphuric acid, which is one of the most important chemicals in our industrial economy. Thousands of tonnes of this chemical are produced each day, in the aggregate, at Canada's various base metal smelters and refineries. The flue gases from roasters, sintering plants, blast furnaces, reverberatory furnaces, and converters are in general passed through electrostatic precipitators for the recovery of up to 95 per cent of the particulate dusts. These dusts are returned for processing to recover the vestiges of metals that they contain.

The remaining clear gases, which are high in sulphur dioxide, are then passed through an oxidation process which results in the production of sulphur trioxide, which dissolves in water to form sulphuric acid. Some of this acid is sold to the general chemical trade or commerce, but at Trail, British Columbia, some forty-five years ago Cominco developed a large plant in which their acid is used in the manufacture of a wide range of agricultural fertilizers. Thus, this waste product is turned to good account.

Now, all industrial processes are not quite perfect, and while it is economically feasible to reduce the sulphur dioxide content of stack gases to about two per cent, a reduction below that level presents difficulties at the present time, although a large body of research is being directed to the problem. Hence, the gases are discharged to atmosphere with a moderate proportion of sulphur dioxide still contained. The discharge is effected through tall stacks which ensure that the gases are emitted at high velocities, temperatures, and altitudes to assure their adequate dispersion and dilution, under even the worst weather conditions. As an example, a few short years ago, Inco erected at Copper Cliff a 381-meter stack, the tallest in the world, at a cost of about $17 millions (Fig. IX-2).

Research in the general area of smelter gases is directed to the problem of removing the "last squeak" of sulphur dioxide, and at the moment it is still in the laboratory stage. One measure which offers some promise is a "sulphite-bisulphite" process, and another has the objective of reducing that last bit of elemental sulphur.

Uranium Mining and Treatment

Uranium ores are similar to base metal ores with respect to their association with iron sulphides, and from the environmental standpoint much the same kinds of problems obtain, but with added complexities. Our largest uranium field is at Elliot Lake in Ontario, where uranium is recovered from an acid-leach process, incorporating ion exchange from purified solutions.

Uranium ores contain a series of disintegration products which are beyond the scope of this book. Even in small quantities, however, these derivatives can be harmful to such things as fish, even apart from the effects of their daughter radioelements.

Fortunately, the acids generated in tailings impoundments do not appear to be severe, but considerable attention is paid to the thorough neutralization and precipitation of effluents from the treatment plants. This is not to minimize the problems, but the principal ones seem to lie, at least for the present, in the occupational environments in the mines themselves. Here, of course, a great deal of effort and vigilance are maintained to see that adequate ventilation is supplied.

Furthermore, consideration must be paid to the general affect on the environment, and this area is being closely monitored by the industry and governmental agencies.

Industrial Minerals

The so-called "industrial minerals" include a wide range of non-metallics which include asbestos, salt, gypsum, magnesite, and a number of others.

Asbestos has been very much in the news as a recognized hazard to health, and the guidelines with respect to acceptable levels of concentration of asbestos fibres in the air, have been continually reduced to the present standard of two fibres per cubic centimetre of air.

Asbestos recovery is carried out entirely in the dry state, by successive stages of crushing so as to minimize degradation of the fibres.

Between the various crushing operations, the ore is passed over screens from the decks of which the fibres are "aspirated" by air suction. The tonnage of air used in the process is commonly ten times that of the rock being treated. In the fairly distant past, the discharge to atmospheres in the vicinity of the asbestos mills contained a fair amount of asbestos fibres, mixed with a larger quantity of other dusts created in the crushing.

The environmental problems arise almost entirely in the handling of these large volumes of air with their entrained dusts. Over the years much effort has been applied, and a great deal of money spent, on the construction and refinement of dust filtration plants and electrostatic precipitation. These, combined with the "pull-through" principle of mill air circulation, represent a considerable improvement.

In one plant of special interest in the Eastern Townships of Quebec, the bag filtration equipment includes 70,000 cotton tubes, each 15 centimeters in diameter and 4 meters in length, amounting to 120,000 square meters of filtration area. In principle, this is typical of the industry which has directed much effort to detailed areas of plants and processes in order to meet the guidelines that have been imposed.

Iron Mining

Iron ores, as required by the buyers, are fortunately free from sulphur. Hence the main problems are concerned with the water discharged from the relatively simple gravity and magnetic concentration

Figure IX-2 — This 381 meter high chimney was put into operation at Sudbury, Ontario, by Inco in 1972 to replace the three obsolete stacks, now capped. The chimney and associated gas cleaning system are a major part of the company's environmental control program.

Chapter IX-3 — Housewives in the Sudbury area, Northern Ontario, admire display of garden flowers.

processes, and from pelletizing plants.

The potential pollutants are particles of stable iron oxides, such as the minerals hematite, specular hematite, with minor amounts of magnetite. They settle relatively rapidly, and thus the effects do not in general persist at very great distances from the point of discharge.

Summary

We have discussed the principal sources of pollution in the mineral extractive industries, and in reasonably simple terms. As has been pointed out, most of the industry's problems arise from the presence of sulphur. In this connection, the burning of coal, oil, and gas as domestic and transport fuels accounts for about sixteen times as much sulphur as do our mineral processes.

This is not to say that there is not much still to be done, but a great deal of effort and money are put into research and development with regard to the various kinds of pollution. Between 1971 and 1975, for instance, some $500,000,000 was spent on environmental control measures by Canadian mining companies. Nowadays, capital expenditures for new plant include up to 20 per cent for environmental considerations.

CHAPTER X

Working in the Mines

Perhaps, because in Canada most mines are located far from the urban centres, mining tends to be viewed in an aura of romanticism by many Canadians — and a miner's calling, because it is an unknown quantity, is looked on as adventurous, even mysterious. But, mining is a business that calls for similar attributes and skills that are required in the more familiar industrial trades or technical professions.

It is in the conditions under which it is practised that mining differs from other industries. The underground workings of a mine present an alien environment to the uninitiated. It is dark. In fact, it is hard to conceive the absolute blackness that prevails underground if one should be left temporarily without a light. Very often the mine is damp, with water dripping off its walls. And, the noise can be deafening if one is close to a drill or other operating machine, because in the confined space there is no place for the sound to go.

But, it is just this type of environment that makes the miner the special breed of workman that he is. He appreciates the fact that, come summer's heat or winter's cold, the temperature remains unfailingly at a comfortable level. Nor, does he have to worry whether the sun is shining or the rain is pouring — his working conditions do not vary, and he'll find out soon enough what's going on above ground. And, although his drill makes a racket when it is operating, when shut off he is left in complete silence, except perhaps for the muted tapping coming through the rock from another drill in a neighboring stope.

The job calls for a person who is independent and self-reliant. Mostly, miners work in pairs or in small groups. If you like to work in crowded conditions and under close supervision, then, this is probably not the job for you. Miners are skilled workmen who can plan and execute their duties on their own, and may be visited by a supervisor not more than a couple of times during a shift.

Mining calls for team work and the miner needs to co-ordinate his work with that of others — perhaps the men on the opposite shift, or the muckers, timbermen, pipefitters, blasters, or other specialists who make up the team. Co-operation is essential since failure in one operation may disrupt the routine, and affect the earnings of others who will not be averse to letting their displeasure be known.

When the miner goes to work he reports to the dry or change house

Figure X-1 — Miners using pneumatic loader for loading holes with explosive slurry in plastic cartridges.

where he changes from his street clothes to his working outfit. This is also where, when coming off shift, he cleans up, has a shower, and soaks up some rays from the sun lamp to make up for the hours of sunlight he missed when underground. To go into the mine he wears warm underclothes, a coverall suit that is lightweight but strong, steel-toed rubber boots, and gloves. He straps a heavy leather belt around his waist which supports a battery pack for his head lamp. He wears a hard hat, or helmet, to which his lamp is attached, carries safety glasses, and ear plugs or covers for noise protection. If the working place is likely to be wet he will wear a coat and pants of waterproof oilskins.

The men and women — yes, they work on surface and underground, too — employed in mining must have good health. Although increasing mechanization has reduced the amount of hard, physical work required, the individual must have reasonable strength and good hearing and eyesight. A physical examination is required by law on starting to work, and medical checkups are carried out on a regular basis.

All activity carries with it risks to safety and health. And, because of the inherent risks associated with mining the development of safe job procedures, combined with common sense, has always been emphasized. Accident prevention and safety are the responsibility of everyone involved — and management, workers, unions and governments cooperate to develop the safest environment possible. The problems of industrial health are still not fully understood and there is much to be learned. In certain mines, the worker may be exposed to silicosis, a disease of the lungs caused by breathing silica dust, or asbestos fibres or radioactive particles in the air. Adequate ventilation is generally the answer, but mining companies, unions and governments are working with research organizations in order to assure that working conditions reach the optimum level.

Although unskilled workers can enter the mine labor force with a minimum of primary school education, the increasing complexity of mine equipment indicates that those who wish to advance to the more highly skilled and better-paid jobs should have secondary school education. Technical training such as is available in technical high

schools and colleges is an advantage and, of course, obtaining a higher level of education through earning an engineering or professional degree at university, broadens the horizons open to the embryo miner.

Mining companies provide the inexperienced worker with a period of initial training. This may include an introduction to the basics of mining, classroom study on surface and underground, followed by on-the-job training as helper to an experienced miner.

Fundamentally, mining involves the breaking of rock and transporting it to surface where it is

Figure X-2 — An operator in a crushing plant wearing an "airstream helmet" for protection from dust.

treated in the mill and smelter for recovery of the valuable metals. To drive the openings underground, machines drill small diameter holes in which explosive material is inserted for blasting to break the rock. The drills may be simple, single machine jack leg drills, operated by compressed air, or they may be the more complicated multi-drill machines operated by either air or hydraulics. After blasting, the broken ore is loaded by air-driven, or hydraulic, mucking machines into trains of cars which are pulled by electric or diesel-powered locomotives.

In mines operated on the trackless mining system, instead of trains of ore cars pulled on tracks by locomotives, LHD (load-haul-dump) machines are employed. The LHD machine (one make is known as a Scooptram) uses a low profile frontend loader; it travels on rubber-tired wheels, and delivers its load to the ore pass or loading pocket at the shaft (Figure VII-12).

In the stopes where the ore is being mined, machines drill long holes for blasting. The broken ore drops by gravity to the level below. Sometimes, slushers, or scrapers — heavy steel blades pulled by a cable operated by a small drum hoist — drag the broken ore to a raise or chute from which it is recovered for eventual transportation to surface.

All of these functions require specialized operators. They all fill the bill as miners but some will be called drillers or drill operators, muckers or mucking machine operators, or the operator of some particular machine, such as a continuous miner which has a huge

revolving head fitted with cutting teeth which literally eats into the bed of potash or coal, or other relatively soft material being mined.

Then, there are a host of service trades such as the blasters and timbermen who fashion the timber supports needed in some mines, the pipefitters who lay the pipes that supply water and compressed air to the drills, the electricians, carpenters, tram crews, maintenance men, and so on.

In surface mining, the jobs are much the same. Except, the scale of the equipment can be very much larger. Bulldozers, loaders, huge trucks carrying several hundred tons in each load, giant shovels which scoop up tens of tons in a single bite, big rotary drills for drilling the blast holes, and all the supporting staff needed to maintain these operations. As mentioned earlier, with power actuated equipment, women have taken their place alongside men in driving the huge trucks and other equipment. As with most mining jobs, one of the qualifications is not to be afraid of getting one's hands dirty.

Besides the miners and various machine operators, there are the technical and professional staff whose duties encompass such operations as sampling, surveying and drafting. And, directing these activities are the mining engineers and geologists who map the progress of the mining operations, design the mining methods, and direct the search for new ore.

Mining involves a little bit of many engineering disciplines. Thus, a mining engineer is something of a jack-of-all-trades. He has to deal

Figure X-3 — A draftsman at his drawing board.

with electrical and mechanical problems as well as mining procedures and geology. Furthermore, being in an isolated community he may be called upon to fill in as a town engineer when the sewage system is in need of repairs, or the water supply is in danger of being interrupted. Of course, the large mines employ electrical and mechanical engineers to look after these special functions, as well as chemical and metallurgical engineers, physicists and others with training in particular fields.

The treatment of ore demands another set of skills. So, in the crushing plants and mills, we have crusher operators, ball mill operators, flotation and solution operators, the latter being involved in overseeing the physical and chemical operations required to recover the concentrates containing the valuable metals and minerals. A

necessary adjunct are the assayers and chemists who carry out the assaying and analysis of samples for the control of the milling and mining operations.

And, when the concentrates are shipped to the smelter, another team of workers comes on the scene — furnacemen, equipment operators, roaster and refinery operators. Automatic controls are common in mills and smelters, so we have control board operators who monitor a whole sequence of operations from a panel of instruments which keep tab on what is happening in various parts of the plant.

But, before we have mines, or mills, or smelters an orebody has to be found. That is the function of the prospector and the exploration team composed of geologists, geophysicists, and geochemists, to

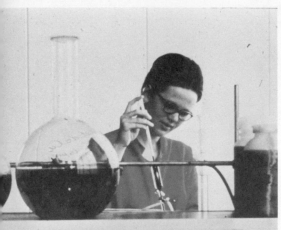

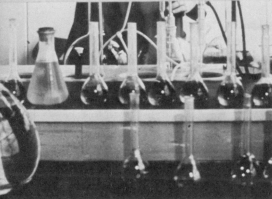

Figure X-4 — Chemist carries out analytical procedures.

Figure X-5 — Operator of heavy equipment in open pit has lofty view of proceedings.

say nothing of the ubiquitous mining engineer. People engaged in these operations will often spend most of their time in remote areas, which is not to say that orebodies cannot be found close to towns or mining centres.

The individual prospector who packs his supplies into a canoe and heads into the bush for a season's work is now a vanishing breed. Although his contribution is still useful, more and more he is being supplanted by the scientific methods which employ various sophisticated geophysical techniques. Aerial surveys covering hundreds or thousands of square miles are used to define the more likely areas where interesting conditions can be followed up by more detailed investigation on the ground involving prospecting, geological mapping and geophysical surveys. This may be followed by diamond drilling, which obviously involves the diamond driller, like the miner, a self-reliant and independent person. He spends much of his time in field camps and is accustomed to moving from job to job since diamond drill contracts seldom last a long time. In all field camps, whether engaged in exploration activities or diamond drilling, one of the most important members is the camp cook whose offerings play a large part in sustaining the morale of the crew.

CHAPTER XI

Selling the Product

As in any other sector of industry and commerce, metals and minerals have to be sold before their values can be realized in terms of cash. While it is impossible in this brief space to take the reader through many of the intricacies of what is perhaps the most complex of all commodity trades, it is the purpose of this chapter to give an introduction to the terminology and perhaps the beginning of an elementary knowledge of metal markets themselves. In a previous chapter we have discussed the relation between a mine producing a copper concentrate and the smelter to which that concentrate may be sold, and that is a fair point of departure.

By far the most important international terminal market for base metals is the London Metal Exchange, London, England. The Exchange has a membership of many firms specializing in the purchase and sale of metals in all of their forms, and various other mineral commodities. In general, the LME functions in a manner similar to our familiar grain exchanges, and many of the same sorts of devices are in use as traders seek the best advantages, and protection against fluctuations in prices.

This procedure refers particularly to **futures,** whereby a buyer purchases a warrant for so many tonnes of metal which is not necessarily in existence at the moment, for delivery at some time in the future, usually three months hence. The price offered will be different – usually, higher – from the prices offered for metal on immediate or **spot delivery**. Such futures, and the warrants representing them are negotiable in the same way as spot metals, and again, the same reasoning underlies their trading. That is, traders seek protection against unfavourable price fluctuations as they may occur, by hedging against current sales.

The London Metal Exchange, it may be said, sets the current prices for Europe and much of the world, and its price quotations represent the actual purchases recorded from day to day, and are made public. The metals traded on the LME are copper, lead, zinc, tin and silver. It has recently expanded its trading activity to include aluminum and nickel.

On this side of the Atlantic, the New York Commodity Exchange (Comex) in recent years has become a major hedge market for such metals as copper, silver and gold. Other organized exchanges are: the

Figure XI-1 — Zinc slabs ready for market.

New York Mercantile Exchange (for platinum, palladium and gold), International Monetary Market of the Chicago Mercantile Exchange (gold), the Chicago Board of Trade (copper, silver and gold), and the Winnipeg Commodity Exchange (gold).

These exchanges are basically hedge markets. A miniscule tonnage of the total sales on the hedge markets is actually delivered. Much of the sales for physical supplies in fact are handled by New York-based metal traders and/or producers. The merchant metal price generally fluctuates daily in line with movements on the LME and U.S. commodity exchanges. Producers have a fixed published quotation which changes only a few times during a year.

Sales for spot metal are also made on the basis of prices published in Metal Bulletin (London), Metals Week and American Metal Market (New York), and The Northern Miner (Toronto).

Metals Week, a subsidiary of the technical monthly periodical, Engineering and Mining Journal, gathers data on virtually all sales made in the United States, and is thus able to publish authoritative average prices in daily, weekly, and monthly terms.

In Canada, the only metal exchange is the Winnipeg Commodity Exchange where trading in gold futures is handled. The press publishes prices quoted by the producers, and these published quotations are sometimes used as the basis for settlement of delivery contracts.

Units Used in the Trade

The actual metal or mineral content of a commodity is of course a function of the assay or analytical result, in terms of some unit or weight. In all contracts it is essential that the unit be closely defined, as for instance in the western world alone there are no less than three different kinds of tons used in the mineral trades.

First, we have our ordinary ton, which is more properly known as the **short ton,** of 2,000 pounds avoirdupois. This is the ton applied on this continent to the ores and metals of the major non-ferrous group, copper, lead, and zinc. In many cases, reference is made to the unit, which in this usage represents one per cent of a ton, or 20 pounds, though it is usually necessary to specify this as a **short ton unit** to distinguish it from others.

Then there is the long ton (2,240 pounds) which, though not confined to any particular geographical area, is the standard in several trades on this continent, notable among which is iron ore. It is also used throughout the world in the commerce of ores of manganese and chromium. The long ton also has its **long ton unit,** which is equivalent to 22.4 pounds.

In most of the world, however, a different ton is used which is gradually being adopted by the industrial world, including Canada and the United States. This is the metric ton, or tonne, which weighs 2,204.6 pounds, or 1,000 kilograms. Its unit is not frequently used, but would weigh 22.046 pounds, or 10 kilograms.

The terms short ton unit and long ton unit are not archaic expressions designed to confuse, but they make

computations simpler in the many cases where a given quality is specified in quotations for an ore. For example, we may consider a fictitious metal "smarbium" and its ore mineral "smarbite" or "smarbium trioxide". If the price quoted in the trade is $5 per long ton unit of SmO_3 based on a 65% ore, the price per long ton of the ore is simply $5 x 65, or $325 per long ton. If the ore were to assay 67% SmO_3, the price would be $335 per long ton.

The metric system is being adopted at different rates of importunity in various parts of the world. Its complete adoption may be slow in some countries, and perhaps in some mineral trades, and this is why we have described the three kinds of tons.

In many cases, equally important with the content of revenue-producing metals are the contents of deleterious substances, and which may incur penalties. Examples include silica, phosphorus, and sulphur in iron ores, zinc in lead ores and vice versa, and there are many others. Offers to purchase frequently specify penalties to be imposed for amounts of these substances beyond acceptable limits, and which are usually expressed in terms of units.

Let us now turn to a few of the major metals, and we shall pay particular attention to the nomenclature of their trades, as applied in the United States and London. In all cases, foreign exchange adjustments are inherent in prices.

Copper

Several prices are quoted for this metal here and abroad. The most important price in North America is the one which is quoted by the primary producers. The base price is for full plate copper cathodes on a delivered basis. Premiums are charged for other grades. The Canadian and United States producer prices are generally in line with the prices on the New York Commodity Exchange and the London Metal Exchange.

The base price for the red metal traded on Comex and other exchanges is for electrolytic wirebar. Deliveries of other grades are subject to premiums or discounts. This price fluctuates daily. Recently, a number of U.S. producers have abandoned their traditional published price for a Comex pricing base. All U.S. prices are quoted in U.S. funds, while the Canadian producers in their domestic market quote in Canadian funds.

As noted above, the LME still remains the single most important copper market. The bulk of international trade and almost all of the metal imported to North America from overseas is priced on the basis of LME quotes.

Copper on LME is quoted in terms of pounds sterling per tonne of electrolytic wirebar, as well as cathodes. Dealings take place in minimum quantities of 25 tonnes and are restricted to brands of metal which have been approved and registered by LME. Two quotations are given, one for cash or spot delivery, and the other for three months forward. The two prices often contain a considerable spread, depending upon many factors in the complex pattern of world supply and demand, and its outlook as viewed by traders.

All sales of cash metal on the LME, which are due for delivery on the following day must be backed by warehouse warrants. All authorized LME warehouses are good delivery points against any contract and the warrants are negotiable.

Lead and Zinc

Like copper, there are producer published prices for lead and zinc sold in the U.S. and Canadian markets. Sales by foreign producers in North America are generally made at or around the prices quoted by domestic producers. New York traders also handle these two metals at daily fluctuating prices which are generally in line with the LME quotes.

Outside North America, zinc producers sell the metal at a fixed price, commonly known as European Producer Price. There is no such fixed price for lead sales.

The London Metal Exchange is the most important free market for lead and zinc. Price developments there influence producer quotes on this continent. Dealings on the LME are in minimum quantities of 25 tonnes for lead and zinc. Like copper, the prices quoted are for spot/cash and three months forward delivery.

Silver

The price pattern for silver is an exceedingly complex business, bound up as it is in monetary and industrial usages. The metal is quoted in terms of cents per **troy ounce,** a weight used in all precious metal trades, and about 10% heavier than the common or avoirdupois ounce. Note that 400¢ per troy ounce is equivalent to $129 per kilogram.

The prices quoted in New York are those supplied by Handy and Harman, specialists in the buying and selling of precious metals. The firm deals in all sorts of silver-bearing materials including bullion, concentrates, residues, and many other forms.

Tin
One of the most useful of metals is tin, though relatively small quantities are traded as compared with the so-called major non-ferrous metals such as copper, lead and zinc. Again, its terms, whether in New York or London, reflect the major source of production in Malaysia, **Straits tin** being the standard to which all other grades are adjusted.

Iron Ores
An extremely complex trade is that dealing in iron ores which are the ultimate source of steel. It has many sets of specifications with regard to

Figure XI-2 — Covered hopper cars carry Saskatchewan potash to export terminals at Vancouver. Mineral products constitute over half the tonnage carried by Canadian railways.

Figure XI-3 — Manganese nodules, photographed on the sea floor, thousands of feet below the surface of the Pacific Ocean. Besides manganese, the nodules are a potential source of nickel and other metals.

acceptable grades and qualities, both with respect to iron content, and to amounts of contained impurities. An ore which is very low in phosphorus is a **bessemer,** and its opposite is **non-bessemer;** beyond this is **high-phos** ore. Iron ores are also graded according to silica content, which should not exceed 18% at the most.

The standard bessemer and non-bessemer ores contain about 51½% iron and up, and are sold in terms of long tons, usually quoted f.o.b. "lower lake ports", reflecting the geography of the steel industry.

Mention has been made of **pellets,** which are high in favor with steelmakers because of their high grade in iron and other useful features. These are usually quoted in terms of cents per long ton unit.

Two metals which are used extensively in the making of special grades of steels are **manganese** and **chromium.** These are usually imported from overseas in the form of their oxide ores, and the weight unit used for both is the long ton. Other important alloy metals are **tungsten** and **molybdenum.** Almost half of the world's supply of the latter comes from Amax Inc. in Colorado. In Canada, molybdenum production is derived mostly as a byproduct of copper mining.

Chrome used on this continent comes from Rhodesia, South Africa, Turkey, and Russia, and its usual specifications call for Cr_2O_3 content ranging between 48 and 56%. Manganese comes largely from India, and its price is based on MnO_2 content, adjusted for impurities. Tungsten is sold on the basis of content per short ton unit, while molybdenum is generally quoted at a price per pound of molybdenum contained in a molybdenite concentrate carrying a minimum of 85% molybdenite.

Gold

The economic aspects of gold are so hedged about by monetary, economic, and political factors as to bear little discussion here. For many years, until the early 1930s its price was controlled by governments and pegged at $20.67 per troy ounce ($665 per kilo) and all gold produced in Canada was sold to the Royal Canadian Mint.

In 1934, President Roosevelt officially raised the price of gold to $35.00 per troy ounce ($1,125 per kilo) and, in effect, re-established the gold standard which had been displaced by floating exchange rates following World War I.

In 1947, the Bretton Woods agreement ushered in an era of fixed exchange rates whereby various world currencies were exchangeable into the U.S. dollar, which in turn was readily exchangeable into gold.

This system worked well until the late 1960s when speculative pressure against the dollar caused a run on gold. This brought in the two-tier gold system whereby there was an official market for central banks and a "free" market for others. In effect, the U.S. closed its "gold window".

Figure XI-4 — Ingots of ferronickel from Falconbridge subsidiary in the Dominican Republic being loaded for shipment to overseas markets.

Speculative pressures and a faltering U.S. economy forced that government to raise the official price to $US38.00 per troy ounce in 1972 and again to $42.22 the following year . . . in effect, devaluing the dollar.

Uranium

The price of uranium is likewise hedged about by political factors, mostly operating internationally. Although a market does exist for sales of small lots on a spot basis, most uranium is sold under long term contract.

For Canadian producers such contracts must have the approval of the Atomic Energy Control Board which regulates the quantities involved and the price to be paid.

There is thus no free market in the ordinary sense, and all sales in North America are on negotiated contracts, with governments taking a strong position with regard to quantities, prices, and terms.

Whatever the nature of the occurrence of the metal as ore in the ground, its content is always reckoned in terms of pounds of U_3O_8 (uranium oxide) per short ton, and the mine output priced accordingly.

CHAPTER XII

Raising the Finances

Let us now look at some of the more usual means of raising capital for development and equipping for production. It is essential to recognize here that, with one or two important exceptions, mining as a business is just about like any other. One exception concerns the fact that a mine represents a wasting asset in that during the course of production the primary asset which gave it its being, is consumed. Another exception is that the risks are higher, and, particularly at the beginning of the life of the enterprise, the geological risks are at their greatest.

It may be convenient here to follow the financial history of a purely hypothetical situation from its pre-discovery through to some point in its adult life as a successful commercial operation.

The discovery itself may have come about in any of several ways, all costing money and effort. It may have resulted from the efforts of the more traditional kind of prospectors doing a search of an area about which some governmental geological report has aroused their interest; in this they may have been financed by a **grubstake** provided by friends or associates on a participating arrangement. On the other hand, they may be employees, operating on salary and

participation, of the exploration arm of an existing successful mining or holding company. Again, the discovery may have been made through a convergent process involving general geological reconnaissance, airborne magnetometer surveys, ground EM surveys, and perhaps a brief test by shallow diamond drilling. Participation in the fruits of discovery, as a principle, is usually involved in some form and on some agreed scale. However the discovery has come about, it has meant the expenditure of money at the high risks associated. But, with the making of the discovery, a dramatic change comes about, in that notions of participation and equity become spectacularly transformed from the abstract to the tangible.

At this point, our knowledge of the discovery will not be at all large, but let us assume that the indications encourage a decision to undertake a major diamond drilling and underground exploration program involving substantial amounts of money. Our prospectors, and their grubstakers, do not have the resources for such a campaign. Or, in the case of the mining company, it may be desired to confine the risks, which are still high at this stage, to this single adventure. In either case, at this time a limited liability company will be formed, and incorporated under appropriate legislation, and the equity will be vested in a stated authorized number of shares.

Now, in consideration of the money and effort that they have expended thus far in making the discovery, the property will be purchased from these **vendors** and the consideration paid will be so many agreed upon shares in the newly formed company, and let us call it Gorny Mines Limited. The vendors will not be allowed to turn round and sell these vendor shares in the market, but rather these particular shares will be **pooled** or held **in escrow,** usually in the hands of a trust company acting under instruction, until such time in the future as a successful application may be made to the Securities Commissioner for their release. The main reason for this will shortly emerge.

Funds From Underwriter

If, for instance, Gorny Mines Limited is capitalized at 5,000,000 shares, and 1,000,000 shares are pooled or placed in escrow for the vendors' interest, the treasury will contain 4,000,000 shares, and on this or some substantial part of it, the company will have to depend for the raising of the funds with which to pursue the exploration program. This is usually done through an underwriter, who purchases blocks of shares on option at graded prices which must be exercised at stated intervals. In turn, the underwriter finds the market and sells the shares into it, his profit depending upon his selling ability, and of course on the

news made by the Gorny property as the program proceeds. It is readily seen that if all of the vendor shares, or any substantial part of them, were to appear on the market without warning or control, the underwriter would be severely handicapped in his attempts to sell the shares he has taken down, and for which he has put badly needed funds into the Gorny Treasury.

To pursue our example further toward its ultimate great success, let us now suppose that our exploration program has put a major mine in sight — say, one that justifies a production rate of 5,000 tonnes per day. Gorny Mines may still have a million shares in the treasury, and perhaps a small cash balance. But it is now faced with the problem of raising something like $25 to $35 millions for the construction of a major mining and concentrating plant, and all of the other facilities that make up a large mine. At this point there may be a choice of financial mechanisms available, and the one taken will depend very largely on the general appreciation of the property in the mind of the investing public. This in turn involves many factors, important among which are the reputation of the entrepreneurs and that of their engineering judgment, and of course the picture which has been built up in the investing public's mind by the results of the detailed exploration program.

In a very rare case, it may be possible to raise a substantial part of the $25 to $35 millions through the sale of the million shares remaining in the Gorny treasury. Conditions may be such that the sale of these

Figure XII-1 — Silver bullion is weighed at Canadian Copper Refiners, Montreal East, Quebec.

shares, together with a bond or debenture issue, may fill the bill. There are other possible arrangements of various combinations of equity and debt financing.

Often, however it will be necessary to create a large number of new shares, and the simplest way to do this is to re-organize the company. In this case, a new company, New Gorny Mines Limited will be formed and it will have its own share capital structure, and its own entity quite apart from that of the predecessor company. The property and assets of Gorny Mines will be transferred to New Gorny Mines in consideration of some agreed part of the New Gorny shares, to be distributed among the equity holders of the older company. These shares in turn may also be pooled or placed in escrow in the same way and for the same reasons that have been described.

New Gorny Mines Limited then sets out to sell its shares through an underwriter, and if our example is as good as we set out to make it, will be able to raise the necessary funds to acquire and set in operation its productive facility.

If conditions are right, any financing mechanism may include a bond or a debenture issue, arrangements which are referred to as **debt financing.** Debt financing has become increasingly important in Canadian mining, particularly where an exclusive interest is involved, such as between a major company and a subsidiary. In some cases where bond or debenture issues are used, the bond or debenture certificate may have attached to it as an added

Figure XII-2 — The City of Timmins, Northern Ontario, whose mines have produced over $2 billion in gold, most of it at prices much below current value.

inducement a **warrant** or **right** in the purchase of so many equity shares at a stated price if exercised by a stated time. This is exactly the same as applied in other areas of commerce. The warrants or rights are themselves negotiable on the market, and their prices are listed with the share prices of the issues they represent.

This has been a somewhat simplistic account; it does include, however, the main points in mine financing in the ordinary, or traditional way. It should be mentioned here that in more recent years, a property which we have posed here is more likely to be financed on an exclusive arrangement by an existing successful mining or holding company with ample funds in reserve for just such purposes. In such cases participation by the public is relatively limited, or confined to taking interests in the parent company's shares. Loan funds may also be provided by the chartered banks.

CHAPTER XIII

Evaluating
the Project

The mineral industry, by any measure is big, vital, and lucrative, and its rewards are spread across a wide cross-section of our population. Its risks are also great and take many forms, among which the most serious are associated with geological settings and their vagaries, with the behaviour of metal and mineral markets, with transportation to and from remote localities, with refractoriness of ores, and with several others. It is impossible to give in this small space a complete guide to the evaluation of the situations reported on in the press, but we can look at a few at least of the factors and how their behaviour affects evaluation.

Gross Value a Fallacy

Although this applies particularly to base metal ores, one of the most common errors made by the casual reader of mining news is to make a simple calculation from a reported percentage of metal by multiplying it by the current market price, and referring to the product as the **gross value.** For instance a copper ore may be reported at 3.5% copper, (i.e. 35 kilograms of copper in a tonne of ore) and if the current market price for that metal is $1.40 per kilo a simple computation suggests that the ore has a gross value of $49 per tonne. This is fallacious, and in some cases it can be dangerous, for as we shall see, the actual return made by the smelter to which it is shipped for the reduction of its copper content, will likely amount to little more than half of that.

Other Considerations

There is nothing sinister about this, and it is quite apart from the ordinary costs of operation in an efficient mine. In the chapter on smelting, it is expected that the reader will have derived a sense that this is a process that involves costs of energy, fluxes, labor, fuels, and a high proportion of fixed costs in a completely specialized plant. There are also metal price fluctuations to be risked, and there are inevitable metallurgical losses. All of these have to be passed on to the shipper of the concentrates, and this is done through an intricate schedule of base charges, artificial adjustments to assays and prices for settlement, and premiums and penalties for various qualities of material.

To return to our example, let us consider for convenience a batch of 10 tonnes of our 3.5% ore, which will be treated in our flotation plant to produce one tonne of concentrate for shipment to the smelter. So we begin with a total copper content of 350 kilos of copper with a "gross" value of $490. Now no recovery

Figure XIII-1 — A standard zinc die casting forms the base plate of Northern Telecom's Dawn telephone. The zinc base plate is seen at left, and, at right, with the telephone components installed.

process is perfect, and in the concentrating plant there could well be a loss of 15%, or 52.5 kilos, leaving us with 297.5 kilos of copper contained in our tonne of concentrate, which therefore has a grade of 29.75% in copper.

We now have to ship that tonne to a smelter which we will assume to be 1,100 km away, and at 3¢ per tonne-kilometer this will cost $33.

Taking the schedule of one typical copper smelter, we find that there is a formulated deduction from the assay content of 13.5 kilos per ton (for our grade of concentrate), which means that the smelter will pay for (297.5-13.5) or 284 kilos of the copper in our concentrate. Also, as a hedge against fluctuating metal prices, he will pay 7½¢ less than the price current on the settlement date, that is at (1.40-0.075) or $1.325 per

kilo on the 284 kilos, which gives us $376.30. For this grade of concentrate, we find that there is a base treatment charge of $46 per tonne. So here we are:

Smelter payment		$376.30
Less: Treatment charge ..	$46.00	
Penalties*	—	
Freight charges	33.00	79.00
Net Smelter return		$297.30

* Charges for excessive impurities in the concentrate.

Referring this back to the 10 tonnes of ore we started with, we find that our 3.5% ore has a revenue value of $29.73 per tonne, which is but 60% of the $49 we gleefully seized upon in the beginning. And, it is this $29.73 which the mining company gets that must cover its costs of mining, milling, administration etc., and provide a

Figure XIII-2 — A prefabricated plumbing unit, left, consisting of copper pipe and tubing, ready for installation in an apartment complex. Above, copper roofing, noted for its durability and pleasing appearance, has been installed on the Forum amphitheatre at Ontario Place, Toronto. Electrical uses, however, still account for over half the copper consumed.

profit. Hence, the so-called "gross" value is seen to have little meaning, and when the reader comes across bald statements using this term without severe qualification, he should be cautious, if not downright suspicious.

The above does not apply however with anything like the same force to ores of gold, unless we are considering the gold content of a base metal concentrate, again for treatment in a smelter. This is because a very high percentage of the gold contained in the ore is recovered, perhaps as much as 95% or more; it is produced in the form of a saleable bullion and there are no heavy transportation or smelter treatment charges to be absorbed. The same reasoning, perhaps to lesser degree, applies to the ores of native silver, and possibly to a few other precious metals.

Perhaps the main feature which distinguishes a mining enterprise from other businesses is the fact that during production the asset, namely, the ore reserves, becomes consumed, and must some day disappear. Hence, it is usual to refer to a mine as a wasting asset, and it is a one crop resource. This means that, to be economically justifiable, its prospective profits must be sufficient to pay back the capital invested within a reasonable time, in addition to the normal rewards associated with the risk.

Cost-Making Factors

There are so many variables involved in mining costs that it is impossible to suggest what the costs should be for anything but a very specific case, and even then only when complete information is available. All businesses are faced with problems exerted upon them by geographical location, distances from markets and supply points, availability of labor, availability of energy in suitable forms, and climate. Some of these operate with particular force in most mining enterprises, scattered as they are throughout Canada with its own peculiar and general problems of transportation and climate. In addition, mines have technological problems exerted by geological conditions and their vagaries, and by such matters as refractoriness of ores, and justifiable scales of operation.

Many orebodies lie in awkward attitudes, and in particular if they are small, problems in ore handling and ground support may be introduced, as well as the supply of materials to the working areas. As a mine reaches a considerable depth, ground support problems increase in difficulty and complexity, requiring increasing amounts of structural or filling materials, and careful programming of operations. This will become true in all cases of mines which persist to depth, even though during the earlier years of the mine's life cheaper methods may have given good results.

Scale of Operation

In general, it may be taken that the higher the scale of operation, the more efficiently can the factors of production be brought together for a profitable result. The selection of an optimum for a particular situation can be quite complicated. In the case of an ore deposit which is more or less vertical, there is however a good rule-of-thumb which suggests that the daily tonnage rate may reasonably approximate 15% of the number of tonnes indicated or developed per vertical meter of depth. For example, if there is an indication of an average of 6,500 tonnes per vertical meter to some reasonable depth, a daily rate of 1,000 tonnes could be justified. While this is empirical, it has a reasonable basis in such areas as amortization, allocation of resources, continuing exploration and development, production, and in programming.

Related to the scale of operation, in many cases, is the true width in which the ore occurs. Ore in wide stopes may be broken and handled much more cheaply than in narrow occurrences, with respect to direct underground mining costs and in such overheads as supervision. For instance, in cut-and-fill stoping, one mine recently reported a stope output of 7.0 tonnes per man-shift from an ore width of two meters, whereas another mine operating under generally similar conditions but with an average stoping width of five meters, reported a stope output of 27 tonnes per man-shift. These include all operations of drilling and blasting, timbering, and filling, which form the basis of direct stoping costs, but do not include service operations such as transportation, hoisting, etc.

The question of the scale of the operation is also related to the availability of ore blocked out or indicated. Some methods involve the leaving of some of the ore in pillars as a support measure, and there is always the problem as to how immediately this ore can become available to stoping. Some of it may have to be sacrificed altogether, and this brings in considerations of unit grade of ore balanced by the costs of a delayed recovery.

Dilution

Some wallrock conditions may produce a considerable amount of **dilution,** that is unwanted rock mixed with the ore. A ton of dilution in the ore stream has to be transported, or otherwise dealt with at some effort and therefore cost, and it should always be thought of as displacing a ton of revenue ore from the milling plant. The avoidance of dilution always involves some particular means, and may have to be reckoned on a cost basis in relation to an alternative mining method, usually more costly than would otherwise be the case.

Refractory Ores

Some of the most successful mines now operating were commercially worthless until serious metallurgical problems could be overcome. In this the selective flotation process, referred to in a previous chapter, has had perhaps the most spectacular effect of all.

Less dramatic, though still important, are ores from which recoveries are not acceptable until very fine grinding, or in some cases, roasting, is applied. The costs of grinding rise quite sharply with fineness of grind, and roasting in small units can be fairly expensive.

In general, the problem is always to select the best process available for optimum recovery from a given ore, consistent with the economics of the situation.

Remoteness

Other things being equal, the costs of operation at a geographically remote property will inevitably be greater than at one in a more accessible and easily serviced mining area. This comes about in several ways, including the obvious one of transport of personnel and supplies, and of the mine's output. Mines are heavy consumers of electric energy, and transmission costs to a remote property will tend to be heavy. In the extreme example, it may be necessary for a mine to generate its own electricity by diesel engines, which is more costly than hydro generated power. And, the day may come when a small atomic power plant is feasible.

Royalties

Although not often applied to newer enterprises, one should examine prospectuses carefully to see whether royalty payments are involved. These may be imposed by a lessor on a lessee, and may be expressed in terms of a payment of so much per tonne mined and treated, or a stated proportion of the value of production. Royalties may sometimes apply to the use of a particular process or invention.

Geophysical Anomalies

At times, a rather undue emphasis is placed on a geophysical anomaly that has been turned up by a survey. While it may prove to be important on checking by another method, its real significance can only be determined by actual sub-surface exploration, such as diamond drilling. No anomaly per se, can ever be assayed for metal content, and it is unlikely that more than one in a thousand will actually indicate the presence of metal or valuable mineral on a commercial scale. This is not however to decry the usefulness of geophysical prospecting, but it does appeal for a measure of critical judgement.

Favorable Areas

When a man wishes to shoot elephants he goes to elephant country, and by analogy it follows that the best place to look for ore is near known ore. History shows many examples of mining areas which were thought to have been worked out, but which have been revived by the application of new geological knowledge and new exploration techniques. The second round in the lives of many of these areas has been based on the newly-found availability of metals altogether different from those originally produced.

Like much good advice however this can act as a two-edged sword, and a prospectus which claims that a given new property is "adjacent to", or is "on strike with", some famous mine or area, should be carefully checked lest it turn out to be 50 kilometers or more away, and on a different geological structure altogether.

In this chapter there have been outlined some of the more significant factors as they may affect an evaluation of mineral property. A good rule, as in every other situation in human affairs which offers participation in some reward, may be stated, INVESTIGATE BEFORE INVESTING.

CHAPTER XIV

Looking at the Balance Sheet

Great advances have been made in recent years developing financial statements which are easier for the ordinary person to understand, but it is somewhat difficult if the investor does not have a reasonable understanding of the basic principles of accounting. Financial statements are prepared in accordance with generally accepted accounting principles. However, the treatment of various items shown in the statements varies according to circumstances and it is in the variations that comparisons one with another are somewhat difficult.

Laws Specify Disclosure

The laws under which corporations carry on business provide for the disclosure of certain specific information in their financial statements. This development in company law reflects increased interest of the public in financial reporting. It grew from experience with corporate responsibility to the public, with careful assistance and counsel from the legal and accounting professions. Accountants recognize their own responsibility to shareholders and public alike, and have narrowed many areas of difference and inconsistency.

Assets and Liabilities

The **balance sheet** is prominent among the financial statements of a company, and it shows the financial condition at a point in time. The reading list at the end of this book contains a reference to an excellent publication, "How to Read Financial Statements."

A first glance at a balance sheet shows that it is divided into two main sections, "Assets" and "Liabilities", and that the sums of money in their respective totals are exactly the same. A good way of viewing a balance sheet is to think of the **asset** side as a list showing, in monetary terms, what the firm owns. The **liability** side is a statement of what the firm owes, also in monetary terms, as well as the various kinds of obligations which have been incurred in the history of the business, such as capital stock and the various kinds of reserves.

The first classification is called **current assets** and this term is used to designate cash and other assets or resources commonly identified as those which reasonably can be expected to be converted into cash, or sold, during the normal operating cycle of the business. Under **current liabilities** you will find a list of those items which are obligations of the company for items which similarly have entered into the operating cycle. These consist of accounts and wages payable, provision for taxes, sinking fund payments, etc. The difference between the total current assets and total current liabilities is commonly referred to as **working capital.** Working capital identifies the relatively liquid portion of the enterprise's total capital.

Items of cash and receivables are shown at their full realizable value. Investments shown under current assets are from cash available for current operations — short term deposits, notes, etc. Precious metal companies show the current market value of gold, silver, or concentrates on hand, or shipped and awaiting settlement. Base metal companies show refinery settlements at realizable value, and metals on hand, or inventories of raw materials and products valued at cost, or market price, whichever is lower.

Investments include marketable securities, such as bonds and shares of a nature precluding them from classification as current assets, or shares in other mining companies, subsidiaries, or associated companies. The balance sheet or book value of these investments is usually at cost, but if some other method is used it should be so indicated on the financial statement. For marketable securities, the indicated market value as of the balance sheet date should be shown.

In the category of investments, appraisal of the value of company shares can be exceedingly difficult. If a complete list of investments is shown the task is much easier, but if the information is given by means of separate financial statements indicating the degree of ownership, then the investor can only determine a reasonable value by doing a lot of pencil work.

The assets, liabilities and income of subsidiaries which are significant to the total business of the company are usually consolidated with those of the parent. For this purpose, a subsidiary is a company in which more than 50% of the voting shares are held. However, an ownership much less than 50% in another company can be of major importance; in fact, often of more value than other companies in which a much larger investment is held.

Mining companies frequently hold shares in other mining companies, some of which may be in the development stage. The value shown is usually the cost of these investments. It may be impossible to place a current value on such investments and only a proper appraisal of the prospect would provide the information the investor requires. Usually he is satisfied to study the reports of the president and consulting mining engineer and judge for himself.

The investor should look carefully at this class of investment and determine, if possible, whether its value might be much greater than the book value or cost shown on the balance sheet.

On the other hand, the reverse could be true and prospects, the value of which might be questionable, may be shown at a figure considerably in excess of what might actually be realized from them. It is common for mining

Figure XIV-1 — The trading floor of The Toronto Stock Exchange where transactions involving the purchase and sale of millions of shares are handled each day.

companies to make substantial advances to other mining companies for the purpose of exploring and developing their properties. The investor should consider the value of these advances in the same relation as the commercial possibilities for the investment itself.

Fixed Assets

Under the heading of capital assets — sometimes referred to as **fixed assets** — we first find a class called mining properties. These are usually shown at cost, but the investor must realize that the cost of mining properties can be either in cash or shares. Shares are often issued for mining properties. The cost of mining properties in such a case is the value at which the shares are issued and this should be approximately the same price as received from shares sold for cash around the time the properties are acquired.

Next are plant, buildings and equipment. These are also shown at cost, and invariably accumulated depreciation is deducted from their cost to indicate net book value.

Other Assets

Another item commonly found on mining companies' balance sheets is a figure for prospecting and exploration on outside properties. Some companies charge all such expenditures to the income account in the year in which they are incurred; others defer certain expenditures until the properties are either proven or abandoned. On being deferred the expenditures show up as an asset on the balance sheet, but the investor should examine the available information and treat them as an asset only in the light of the explanations given in the annual report.

Under the classification of other assets you will very often find an item such as preproduction and deferred development expenditures, less amounts written off. These items can have several meanings. In the case of a new mine, preproduction charges represent the costs of exploration and development prior to the time the mine comes into production. Deferred development can be either in the same category or it can be a similar treatment in an established mine where expenditures are laid out to develop orebodies which may not be touched for some years to come. In certain cases it would be incorrect to charge such expenditures to the ore currently being removed since in effect an additional capital investment in the mine is being made.

Current Liabilities

Turning now to the liability section of the balance sheet we find a variety of items under **current liabilities.** These consist of obligations due for payment within a period of about 12 months. Accounts and wages payable occupy first place, being most current, but if the company has borrowed from the bank on current account you will find the first item as a bank loan. If the company treats

ore on a customs basis you will find particulars of its liability to customers for outstanding ore settlements. If a dividend has been declared but not yet paid, the amount of the dividend is a current liability.

The next item, and a very important one it is, is the estimated liability for income taxes. The amount shown represents the company's estimate of what it owes for taxes for the current year, less any instalments which may have been paid on account, plus provisions for previous years which may not have as yet been assessed by the taxing authorities.

If the company has any bonded indebtedness, then the amounts due on principal account or required for sinking fund payments during the succeeding 12 months would be shown as a current liability.

An item commonly seen on present day balance sheets under liabilities is entitled "provision for deferred income taxes", or "taxes on income deferred to future periods." Some explanation to the investor is warranted concerning this item. When calculating its tax liability, a company can claim depreciation, or capital cost allowance as it is sometimes called, on a different basis from that which it deems proper and justifiable as a charge to the income account. A company usually likes to take full advantage of the maximum rates of capital cost allowance and often it claims depreciation in excess of that charged to its income account. When this occurs its current liability for taxes is reduced, but on the other hand, when the depreciation which may be claimed for tax purposes in the future is less than that reflected in the income account, then taxes will be abnormal in relation to that year's income. Consequently, the difference between taxes payable using normal depreciation and taxes actually paid is charged to income and carried as a deferred credit in the balance sheet. This will be credited to income in future years when the amount of depreciation allowed for tax purposes is less than the amount charged to income in the company's accounts.

Notes payable of a non-current nature or advances from a parent, subsidiary or associated company are shown as separate items under the liabilities.

Long Term Debt

The investor should take careful note of the long term indebtedness, whether it be by mortgage bond, debenture issue or otherwise. Particulars of the maturity dates are shown and the investor should read the balance sheet notes carefully to see if any assets have been pledged as security for the indebtedness. Requirements to meet these obligations may materially affect the funds available for payment of dividends.

Reserves

The investor should look carefully at any reserves he finds in the balance sheet under liabilities and particularly at their explanation. There are numerous types, for contingencies, future losses, inventories, and so forth, and their misuse can arbitrarily reduce income for one year or move it from one year to another. Provision for a reserve properly chargeable against the revenue of one year but not charged to that year's income accounts, creates an understatement of that year's profit. Reserves should not be used to relieve income of future periods of items which are properly chargeable to that year's income.

Capital

Authorized capital constitutes the number of shares which the company is entitled to issue under the terms of its charter. The **par value** of a common share has no particular significance. Mining companies may issue par value shares at a discount, i.e. for less than the $1 or other specific par value per share. The capitalization of some companies may consist of **no par value** shares, although the charter will specify the maximum amount of capital that may be raised. The number of shares issued is the most significant factor, since this figure is required when calculating the net profit per share, or the break-up value per share.

The investor should note whether any shares remain unissued. If a mining company needs additional capital for further development of its properties, it can use these shares to the extent that funds can be raised. If insufficient shares remain in the treasury and the company cannot resort to borrowing, then it may obtain supplementary letters patent to increase the authorized capital. If additional shares are then issued, the original shareholder will suffer a dilution of his equity. Or, the company may be reorganized by arbitrarily reducing the issued shares by one half, or some other factor, and then creating additional new shares which can be sold to raise capital. Approval of a majority of a company's shareholders, as well as the regulatory authorities, is necessary to implement these measures.

Don't overlook reading the auditors' report to the shareholders. If there is any divergence from recognized accounting principles, the auditors would draw attention to this. Such an event seldom occurs among well regulated corporations.

Before passing from the balance sheet, be sure to take a look at the comparative figures. They will quickly show you whether working capital has been increased or decreased and similar analysis can be made of capital assets, investment and liabilities.

Statement of Income

The statement of income or profit is perhaps more readily understood by the investor but there are some items, the treatment of which could materially affect your analysis. The income account will tell you the results of the business for a specific period, usually 12 months, but real profits are not fundamentally the results of operations for such a short period. Progress can only be measured by comparisons with the previous period or a number of periods with due recognition given to factors which might tend to distort the comparison. It is hazardous to place too great a reliance on net income as shown by a single annual statement.

The income account first shows the amount received or to be won from metals produced during the year. To this is usually added items of other revenue attributable to operations. Under expenditures you will find the costs of production, including mining, current development, crushing, conveying, milling, administrative and general corporate expenses, marketing expenses, royalties and real property taxes. If funds have been borrowed to carry on the business, then the interest on bonds or debentures would be included.

Depreciation

To these costs is then added **depreciation,** which is an amount set aside or appropriated out of income. There are a variety of opinions, even among the experts, as to the true meaning of depreciation and a whole chapter could be written on this alone. However, fixed assets historically have been accounted for on the basis of cost, and a simple explanation of this item would be to say that it represents the current year's share of the original cost of capital invested in buildings, plant and equipment. The rates for mining companies are higher than for ordinary companies because of the shorter life usually encountered. Different rates apply to different classes of fixed assets, but in general the charge is equivalent to 10% or 15% of original cost. In theory, after the cost of an item of equipment has been fully depreciated, at which time the item will then have come to the end of its useful life, the company will have the funds on hand to purchase a replacement.

Figure XIV-2 — Development of Canada's huge reserves of oil contained in oil sands will require the expenditure of billions of dollars. This is the business end of a bucket wheel excavator at Fort McMurray, Alberta, mining oil sands at the rate of over 7,000 tonnes an hour.

After all the above costs are deducted from the revenue from metals produced, we arrive at a figure commonly referred to as operating income or profit derived from mining operations. From this it is usual to deduct extraordinary expenditures, such as cost of internal shafts, or other unusual expenditures not capitalized, expenditures on outside exploration and write-offs. **Write-offs** are usually for preproduction or deferred development and these are charged to current income account on some predetermined basis, either percentage-wise or on a tonnage formula.

Income from investments is added to the net operating profit and income taxes are usually the last item shown. The final figure, which is net income, represents the profit for the year. This is transferred to surplus or shareholder's equity account, which is likewise reduced by any dividends which are paid. Net income per share is usually shown, but if not the figure can readily be ascertained by dividing the net income by the number of issued shares.

To ascertain the **cash flow,** the investor should start with the net income figure as shown, and add to it those items which do not constitute an outlay of cash during the year. These items would include depreciation and such write-offs as preproduction and deferred development. The result is cash flow or cash generated by the business during the year. The disposition of this cash can be found by analyzing the comparative balance sheet. Funds might be used to purchase investments, repay advances, meet obligations on long term debt, acquire additional plant and equipment, or pay dividends to shareholders. Any difference in the application of funds would be represented by an addition or reduction in the company's working capital. Many companies include in their annual report a statement showing the source and application of funds for the year and such statements are helpful to the investor.

From all this it will be realized that there is no ready and easy way to analyze a mining company's financial statements. The facts are presented as best as can be, at all times taking into account basic recognized accounting principles. In the long run the only way in which the value of a mining share can be measured is by reference to the amount of distributable profits available for payment of dividends. Financial statements seldom if ever reflect the value of intangibles. These intangibles affect future earning possibilities from the investment of original capital or by re-investment of profits in the business.

The goal of mining is profit. Minerals in the earth can invariably be recovered, but the work will not be undertaken unless a profit can be expected. Finance, therefore, dominates the process of extraction and all operating procedures are restrained by financial considerations. In consequence, mine economics occupies an important part of a mining company's work and regardless of the risks involved those who prospect for, explore and develop Canada's mineral resources have usually given a good account of their actions.

The investing public holds the scales to judge the relative merits of a mining enterprise, but the investor must be properly informed. Financial statements can be of great assistance to those who take the time to study them.

THE MINING NORTH (top):
Scenes at Elliot Lake, Ontario.
CAREERS (below): Surveyor;
engineers examine mine
model; tyro hockey players;
miner tightening roof bolt;
power shovel operator;
technicians in assay
laboratory.

THE OIL BUSINESS (Clockwise from top): A gas well drilled from ice on Parsons Lake in the Mackenzie Delta, N.W.T. Drill ship, Canmar Explorer I, in the Beaufort Sea. Mammoth tanker unloads oil from Arabian Gulf at Point Tupper, Nova Scotia, refinery. Wildcat well drilling at Ghost Pine, Alberta.

CHAPTER XV

Canada's oil heritage

Next to water, petroleum is perhaps the most valuable natural resource known to mankind. Without petroleum, modern life as we know it would come to an abrupt halt.

Petroleum heats our homes, runs our cars, trucks, trains and planes, provides material for tires, the roads and highways we travel on, generates electricity and puts clothes on our backs. From the moment that your plastic alarm clock goes off in the morning to the time you put on your polyester pyjamas at night, petroleum and its estimated 3,500 byproducts influence our daily lives. Through this multitude of products and uses, petroleum is an integral part of the way of life of every Canadian.

No one knows for certain when mankind first came to use petroleum. Records go back as far as 6000 B.C. when asphaltic oil was used to waterproof shipping vessels. It is also known that the Egyptians used petroleum as an embalming agent for mummies and as a fortifying agent in the construction of the pyramids. Whatever its earlier uses, petroleum really came of age following the rapid industrialization in the early 20th century.

Like all industrialized nations, Canada is dependent on crude oil as its primary source of energy. Natural gas, a relative newcomer to the energy scene, is rapidly emerging as the second major source of Canadian energy. Combined, crude oil and natural gas provide more than 65% of Canada's energy requirements and will continue to do so for some time to come.

Oil was first discovered in North America in 1858. Drilling near Oilsprings, Ontario, James Miller Williams found oil at a depth of approximately 60 feet. The father of the modern oil industry, Williams produced and refined his product to sell as lamp oil. Following the initial Oilsprings discovery, several subsequent finds were made in nearby Petrolia, Ontario. Though speculation and exploration increased, Canada's contribution as a major oil producer was shortlived. Canada may have launched North America's first oil boom, but developments in the United States quickly overshadowed Canadian efforts. In 1859, oil was discovered in Pennsylvania and the American industry was off to a roaring start. Production from Oilsprings and Petrolia could not keep up with demand and Eastern Canada was soon forced to rely on imports from the United States to supplement its production.

By the turn of the century, the focus of the industry shifted to the Canadian west.

The Canadian Pacific Railway, while drilling for water near Medicine Hat, Alberta, inadvertently hit natural gas in 1883. The first oil discovery was found in Waterton National Park in 1902, but it was the famed Turner Valley discovery in 1914 that launched the first real oil boom in western Canada. More than 500 companies were formed within months, but again the boom was brief.

Then there was the Norman Wells in the McKenzie Basin, only 90 miles south of the Arctic Circle. That discovery well, put down in 1920, yielded 54,000 barrels of top grade oil before it was abandoned in 1944. While not a mega field, it is respected by oil men, for it is still producing some 3,000 barrels daily with plans for expansion. In fact, reserves here are presently estimated at 650 million barrels.

But there were really no major discoveries in this country until 1947 when, after drilling 133 'dry' holes, Imperial Oil struck the largest Canadian field at Leduc just south of Edmonton.

Leduc turned out to be one of Canada's largest oilfields. Its discovery ushered in the beginnings of the modern Canadian petroleum industry and Alberta's wealth. During the three decades following the Leduc discovery, many other fields were found in western Canada: Redwater, Golden Spike, Rainbow, Swan Hills, Excelsior, Joseph Lake, Stettler, Bonnie Glen, Wizard Lake and others. Throughout the 1950s, 1960s and 1970s,

new oil and gas discoveries were made, adding large reserves to Canada's energy supply system. By the late 1960s, Canada's northern frontiers began to interest explorers.

Western Canada's last major oil discovery was made in 1965 at Rainbow Lake in northwestern Alberta. Ironically, while activity moved to the frontiers, two major discoveries were made in the late 1970s in the Alberta Basin. The first was West Pembina, a field adjacent to Pembina, one of Canada's largest producing fields which was discovered in 1953. The second was the discovery of a major gas field in the Elmworth area of northwestern Alberta. The potential reserves of the Elmworth field rival those of Alberta's largest established gas fields. These finds have spurred new interests and prospects for the industry and exploration aggressively continues on all potential fronts.

In Canada, oil and gas are found in areas known as sedimentary basins. These are areas that at one time were covered with ancient seas teeming with marine plant and animal forms. Over millions of years, this organic matter was buried in the sea beds and became blanketed in layers of sand, silt and mud. These sediments eventually turned into sandstone, limestone and shale, and the organic matter, through the processes of bacterial action, heat and compression, formed gaseous and liquid hydrocarbons.

Most of Canada's known reserves of crude oil and natural gas have been found in the vast Western Sedimentary Basin covering northeastern British Columbia, Alberta, the southern half of Saskatchewan and the southwestern corner of Manitoba. Similar sediments exist in the Yukon and Northwest Territories, the Arctic Islands, the Beaufort Sea, Hudson's Bay and off the west and east coasts of Canada. Petroleum exploration activity is under way in all these areas.

Oil and gas are not found as underground lakes or pools, but are trapped in tiny pores between the crystals of grains of rocks. Crude oil can be found in a variety of colors and consistencies. It may be yellow, green, brown or black in color; it may resemble water or be as thick as molasses. In its pure state, natural gas or methane is colorless, odorless, tasteless and lighter than air. It is often accompanied by other hydrocarbons such as butane, propane, pentane and sulphur.

On the world energy scale, Canada is actually a small player in terms of petroleum production. Though the largest per capita energy consumer, Canada only possesses about 2% of the entire known reserves of conventional oil. (However, Canada has some of the world's largest conventional heavy oil and oil sands deposits.) The world's largest oil producers are the Soviet Union, Saudi Arabia and the United States in that order. The United States produces about six times as much oil as Canada and the Middle East produces over 14 times as much. Geologists estimate that current world conventional reserves will be depleted in 30 years, but that a like amount remains as yet undiscovered throughout the world. Canadian production of natural gas contributes about 5% of total world production, while production in the United States is seven times greater than Canada's.

Canadian supplies of conventional crude oil have been steadily declining since 1973 while consumption has increased. Like other western nations, Canada has been greatly affected by the disruption of internationally traded oil and the subsequent quadrupling of world oil prices by OPEC in 1973. Currently, Canadian demand exceeds 1.9 million barrels per day while domestic supply, 85% of which comes from Alberta oilfields, is 1.5 million barrels per day. The recent shortfall of 400,000 barrels per day is imported from foreign sources.

At the same time, however, Canada is richly endowed in natural gas and in the early 1980s is experiencing a large oversupply. We also find ourselves in a unique and enviable position with regards to future supplies of crude oil. In fact, while the rest of the work is tied to the whims of the OPEC cartel, Canada has the potential to produce

Imperial Oil Limited Leduc #1 well the day it 'blew in' Feb. 13, 1947

its own vast resources and become self-sufficient in oil

Firstly, there is the possibility of finding new reserves in the Western Sedimentary Basin. By drilling to deeper depths in new horizons, substantial reserves could be added to the supply inventory. There is also the possibility of implementing enhanced recovery schemes to "squeeze" the remaining oil out of existing fields. As it is, only 25% of the oil in place is generally recoverable by natural pressure. Therefore, there is considerable incentive to develop secondary and tertiary recovery schemes to further increase oil recovery.

Canada can also boost of substantial reserves of heavy oil located from the Lloydminster area on the Alberta/Saskatchewan border to the Peace River — Wabasca area in central Alberta. This thick viscous crude, much thicker than conventional oil, will also require special enhanced recovery methods in order to produce the oil in commercial quantities.

In addition, one of the world's largest deposits of oil in the world is located in Canada. The famed Athabaska tar sands may be able to provide over 200 billion barrels of recoverable oil requiring only the right economic climate to spur its development. At the recent rate of consumption, these reserves could well last Canadians for more than 275 years!

The Beaufort Sea, Arctic Islands and the east and west coast offshore areas have excellent potential to add to future oil and gas needs. With the right combination of economics and technology, these frontier areas may be Canada's "ace in the hole" in achieving the goal of oil self-sufficiency.

The great paradox of the Canadian energy situation is that even with abundant resources, not enough oil is being produced to offset the growing energy thirst. Canada continues to wrestle with fluctuating prices and supply and demand imbalances. Economics, technology and politics are the determining factors in future petroleum developments. It will take an all-out co-operative effort of governments, the industry and the consuming public working together to provide a strong energy future.

From the first oil booms of the 1950s, the Canadian petroleum industry has grown and developed the most dynamic and innovative teams of explorers in the world. Though the first players in the search for petroleum were the enterprising multinational companies, the Canadian independent sector came into its own in the early 1970s and continues to be a forceful player in Canadian exploration activity.

Today, there are about 700 companies directly involved in oil and gas exploration and production. There are large, medium and small companies, both public and private, with different corporate philosophies and innovative exploration prospects. It is this competitive keenness that has made Canada's petroleum expertise recognized and respected around the world. It's a vital challenging and exciting industry, with a heavy responsibility to furnish the majority of Canada's energy needs now and in the foreseeable future.

CHAPTER XVI

Petroleum Exploration

The Principles of Petroleum Geology

"There is nothing capricious in nature."

Ralph Waldo Emerson

As a petroleum geologist, one wonders. Nature has a way of barring oil from obvious hiding places and hoarding it in unsuspected corners.

At first glance the principles of petroleum geology are simple:

1. Petroleum liquids (oil) and gases are combinations of hydrogen and carbon. Hydrocarbon compounds are organic substances, not minerals.

2. Hydrocarbons are derived from animal and plant matter of all geological ages, buried in the sediments of ancient oceans. Therefore, oil and gas are most often found together with salt water in, or in close association with rocks of marine origin.

3. At first, the conversion of organic remains into hydrocarbons is the result of bacterial action. The main product is methane (marsh or coal-mine gas). At burial depths of a few thousand meters and temperatures between 50° and 150°C both oil and gas are generated by chemical reactions.

Additional overburden leads to the breakdown of any oil previously formed. The main product is again methane, this time the result of excessive heat.

4. In order to accumulate in commercial quantities hydrocarbons need space, but they do not occur in underground caves and rivers. Petroleum is produced from the **pores** and minute **fissures** of host rocks such as sandstones, limestones and dolomites.

5. The reservoir fluids, gas, oil and water, follow the laws of **gravity.** If all three are present in the same container, gas rises to the top, oil stays in the middle and water rests at the bottom.

6. Since hydrocarbons continue to rise through permeable rocks unless stopped from escaping to the surface, one of the most important requirements for a petroleum reservoir is an impermeable "roof". In order to form a **trap** for oil or gas the roof, viewed from below, must be concave.

The problem is that these subsurface conditions cannot be observed or measured accurately from above. Educated guessing plays a large part in petroleum exploration.

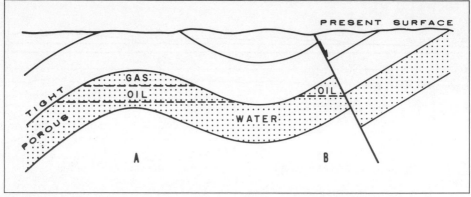

Figure XV-1 — Diagrammatic cross-section showing structural petroleum traps. (A) anticline, (B) fault trap.

Structural Traps

The most obvious petroleum reservoir is a porous rock formation under a tight layer, both folded into a dome-shaped **anticline** (Figure XV-1A). If the entire sequence of sediments above the subsurface anticline has been deformed in the same manner, the structure can be mapped at the surface. So, is there a direct oil-finding method after all? No, because even if a structure has a surface expression, it may lack the right combination of porous and dense rocks or it may be filled with water.

A structural trap can be defined as one whose roof has been shaped by local deformation, not only by **folding,** but also by **faulting** (Figure XV-1B).

Structural traps that can be mapped at the surface are quickly found and the number of undiscovered ones are rapidly diminishing. Oil-finding has become more complicated since it began over a century ago.

Stratigraphic Traps

A different kind of petroleum reservoir owes its existence not to deformation, but to a change or break in the porous formation. It can only be detected by **stratigraphy,** the study of layered rocks, and is therefore called stratigraphic trap.

Primary stratigraphic traps (Figure XV-2A) are a product of the environment in which the sediment in question was laid down. **Sandstone** lenses of all shapes and sizes, for instance, can be the result of wave and current action in ancient oceans, or they can represent parts of buried deltas and river channels. Another common type of primary stratigraphic trap was created by local replacement of dense **limestone** by porous **dolomite.**

Sandstones enclosed in shale and dolomites enclosed in limestone are similar in many respects, at least as far as the trapping mechanism is concerned. Another important group of traps, the **organic reefs,** is somewhat different. In the

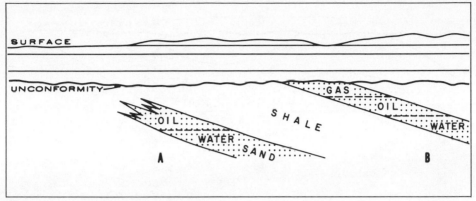

Figure XV-2 — Diagrammatic cross-section showing (A) primary, and (B) secondary stratigraphic petroleum trap.

stratigraphic sense a reef is a mound-like or layered rock structure built by corals and other marine organisms. It can be large, like the modern Great Barrier Reef off the east coast of Australia, or small like the atoll of Bikini. One of the best-known fossil examples is the oil reservoir of Leduc, Alberta. Traps of this nature fall in the primary stratigraphic category, but since they were built up above the surrounding sea floor, often to heights of several dozens of metres, they have much in common with structural traps, and as exploration targets they are in a class by themselves (Figure XV-3).

In contrast to primary stratigraphic traps, **secondary stratigraphic traps** are a product of developments that took place long after the deposition of the reservoir rock. In the most important of these events, ancient layers of sediments were lifted above sea level, exposed to weathering and erosion for a few million years, and then returned to their aquatic environment to be covered with new sediments. The usual result of such "temporary" interruption of the depositional process is an **angular unconformity** between the older and younger sets of rocks. A reservoir rock sandwiched between dense formation, truncated by erosion, and capped by a younger dense layer can become a trap for migrating petroleum (Figure XV-2B).

It is probably clear by now, that most stratigraphic traps could not exist without some structural help, however subtle. Small, steep-sided "pinnacle" reefs and small, completely hydrocarbon-filled porous lenses are the only pools where structure has a negligible effect on the fluid distribution. Widespread sands, on the other hand, can be useless from the standpoint of the petroleum geologist if they lie absolutely flat and horizontal. Only when such a sand has been tilted or folded ever so

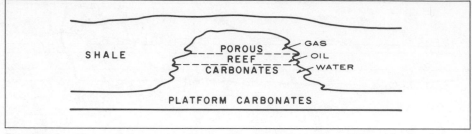

SHALE — POROUS REEF CARBONATES — GAS OIL WATER — PLATFORM CARBONATES

Figure XV-3 — Diagrammatic cross-section through an organic reef as a stratigraphic oil and gas trap.

slightly, can petroleum liquids gather to form a pool. Even in the exploration for stratigraphic traps structure is important.

Oil and Gas in Western Canada

For the majority of oil companies operating in this country, the Western Canada Sedimentary Basin (Figure XV-5) is still the most important hunting ground.

Figure XV-4 — Geologist uses compass to check dip and strike of rock strata.

In Alberta, the first commercial gas field was developed around the turn of the century. It led Rudyard Kipling to remark to the people of Medicine Hat that they seemed to have "all hell for a basement". In the geological sense, of course, the gas occurs high above the basement, in **Cretaceous** beds near the top of the **stratigraphic column** (Figure XV-6), a mere 300 m (984 ft.) below the surface. The thick sand-and-shale sequence of the Cretaceous system contains numerous primary stratigraphic traps, among them the Pembina oil pool, one of the largest in North America.

Following the contours of the Canadian Shield, whose crystalline rocks form the basement of the Western Canada Sedimentary Basin, the "soft rock" cover has a slight southwesterly tilt. This is the regional structural element needed to cause oil and gas to gather near the **updip** edges of Cretaceous sand lenses and similar reservoirs.

Below the Cretaceous, at depths of hundreds to thousands of metres is an unconformity that resulted from the elevation above sea level and erosion of much older Mississippian and Devonian sediments. When the basal

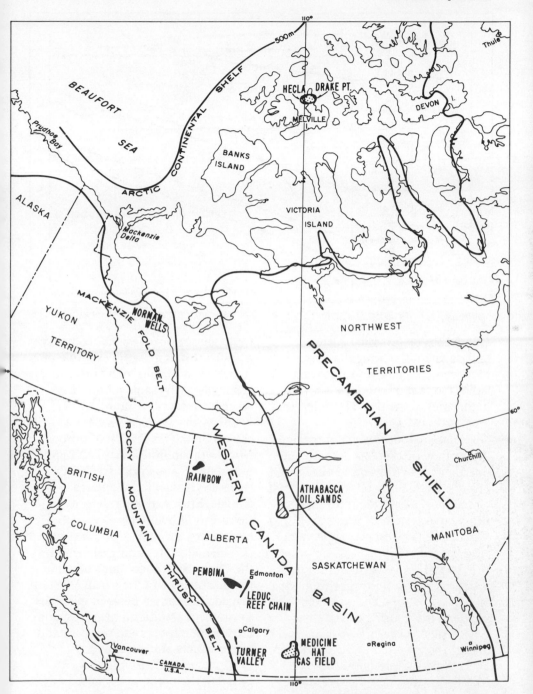

Figure XV-5 — Map of Western Canada showing sedimentary basins under exploration for oil and gas.

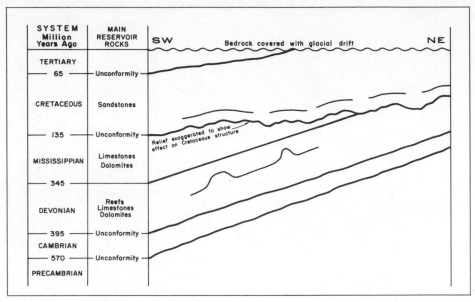

Figure XV-6 — Generalized stratigraphic chart and cross-section through central Alberta.

Cretaceous or Jurassic beds were laid down on this irregular surface, they were draped over ridges and valleys so that oil- and gas-bearing highs often coincide with underlying erosional hills.

Cretaceous rocks account for one third of the marketable gas and one quarter of the recoverable oil reserves of Alberta, but the Cretaceous is only the third most productive system in Western Canada. In this respect too, it comes after the Mississippian.

Mississippian petroleum is produced primarily from two kinds of traps, structural and secondary stratigraphic. During the late Cretaceous and early Tertiary disturbance that led to the formation of the Rocky Mountains, the Mississippian limestones and shales under the Alberta foothills were folded and faulted into large anticlines and thrust plates. The Turner Valley field, whose partial discovery in 1914 touched off the first Canadian "oil boom" (actually a gas boom), is a classic example of a structural trap, and many prolific gas pools of the same nature have since been found (Figure XV-7).

Secondary stratigraphic traps, caused by the truncation of porous Mississippian limestones and their burial under impervious younger rocks are typical for Weyburn, Midale, Steelman and other oil fields in southwestern Saskatchewan.

The major producing system is the **Devonian.** It contains 60% of the oil and 30% of the gas in Western Canada. Devonian petroleum comes mostly from stratigraphic traps, and most important among these are the organic reefs of central and northwestern Alberta, Leduc, Redwater, Golden Spike and many others.

It appears that the ancient reef-building organisms preferred a certain narrow depth range and thrived under certain oceanic

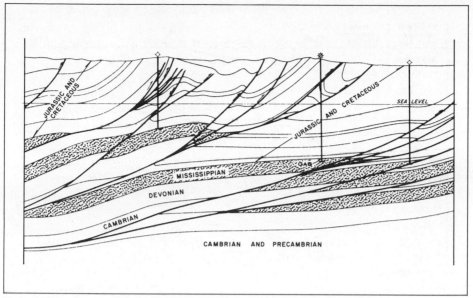

Figure XV-7 — Cross-section showing complicated Foothills structures in western Alberta. (Courtesy Veezay Geodata Ltd., Calgary.)

current conditions, both of which prevailed in linear trends along the bottom of the Devonian sea. This is why the reefs in the Edmonton area are arranged like beads on a string, a fact that made it relatively easy to locate additional reefs once the Leduc discovery had been drilled in 1947.

Other Devonian targets are not so obliging. Some of the West Pembina and Rainbow reefs of western Alberta, for instance, measure only a few hundred meters in diameter, and they are scattered at random throughout their depositional basins.

In northwestern British Columbia, large gas reserves are trapped in the dolomitized parts of an extensive limestone platform. Here, dolomitization follows no recognizable pattern, which makes exploration difficult and costly. The best-known example is the Clarke Lake gas field near Fort Nelson.

Oil Sands

The reserves of conventional oil, oil that can be produced in the traditional manner, are declining rapidly, not only in North America, but throughout the world. Canada is fortunate in being able to offset this decline at least to some degree by gradually bringing vast, but intractable bitumen deposits into production.

Early travellers noticed these hydrocarbons in Cretaceous **tar sands** exposed along the banks of the Athabasca River in northeastern Alberta. They occur at depths down to 750 m (2,500 ft.) in a broad trend from Peace River to Cold Lake. Together they contain about 140 billion cubic meters (880 billion barrels) of bitumen in place, or about 30 times the amount of conventional oil discovered in Alberta.

The special problem with the oil or tar sands is not discovery, but recovery. It is much easier to pump oil out of a solid porous subsurface sandstone than to separate it from a sticky mixture of bitumen, clay and loose sand.

Where the mixture lies at or near the surface as in the McMurray area, it is mined with **bucket wheel excavators** or **draglines** in the largest open pit operations in the world. The bitumen is extracted from the ore by a **hot water** and **steam** treatment and then upgraded to lighter "synthetic" oils suitable for conventional refining (Figure XV-8).

Where the oil sands lie below the reach of surface mining techniques, as in the Peace River and Cold Lake areas, the bitumen will probably have to be steamed into mobility **in situ** (in place) and produced through wells drilled for this dual purpose.

Both methods are complex and costly. They are economic only if the product can be sold at world market prices.

The Northern Frontier

The first oil discovery to speak of in Western Canada was made, not in Leduc, but in another reef at Norman Wells, Northwest Territories, in 1920. Today,the vast region north of the 60th Parallel is still frontier, and the future of the northern Interior Plains as a petroleum province is still in doubt.

Farther north, in the Mackenzie Delta, the Beaufort Sea and in the Arctic Islands, large amounts of gas and some oil have been found and will eventually be produced.

Oil and Gas in Eastern Canada

Canada's oldest oil province, the area between Lakes Huron and Erie is small, and it produces a correspondingly small amount of oil, approximately 150,000 cubic meters (945,000 barrels) per year, much less than the daily potential of Western Canada.

Offshore drilling along the Canadian east coast has been successful in the area of Sable Island and on the Labrador Shelf. Petroleum geologists have high hopes, expecially for the latter region.

Reconnaissance

Petroleum prospecting has been called an art, and it certainly is not all science. It is by no means unusual to see an exploration project "advance" from pure science to all art as different levels of management get into the act and diverse professional prerogatives are exercised.

The systematic search for new oil reserves is conducted in two stages. First, a likely sedimentary basin must be found, and then the most promising drillsites within that basin must be pinpointed. Each phase requires a different strategy.

Government agencies and international oil companies have been busy taking worldwide inventory of possible future petroleum provinces for decades. It is unlikely that sizable accumulations of sediments have escaped their attention.

Prospective basins can be graded by comparing their history, their position with respect to oceans,

Figure XV-8 — This huge bucket wheel excavator mining oil sands at the Suncor Inc. operation near Fort McMurray, Alberta, is over 60 m long, 21 m high and weighs 1,900 tonnes. It can excavate an average of 7,260 tonnes per hour.

mountain belts and continental shields, and their size and shape, with that of already productive basins. That some promising areas are still virtually unexplored is simply a matter of economic and social priorities.

Once a sedimentary basin has been recognized as a potential new petroleum province, the question is what to do next. It is not too often that a drilling contractor can be called in right away to test all those domes, anticlines and fault blocks. If the surface geology within the basin provides enough clues it is relatively easy to make sound drilling recommendations. This has been the case in the Arctic Islands, where lack of glacial debris, soil and vegetation has kept the bedrock bare and revealed dozens of drillable structures.

Explorers in southern Canada are less fortunate. Even if it were not for the thick cover of glacial drift that blankets the prairies, the essentially flat bedrock surface would still mask the few subtle structures that exist underneath. Here, a systematic search would probably begin with an attempt to chart the structural make-up of the subsurface by **airborne geophysical** means.

The fastest and least expensive tool for determining the approximate depth and rough structural grain of an unexplored basin is the **magnetometer,** airborne over land and seaborne offshore. It measures local and regional deviations from the main magnetic field of the earth. Its effectiveness depends on variations in the abundance of magnetite

(Fe_3O_4) and a few other minerals in which most sedimentary formations are lacking. For this reason the instrument can only indicate trends in the composition and architecture of the crystalline basement. These in turn may or may not have had an influence on the overlying strata.

The **gravity meter** responds to differences in the gravitational pull exerted by rocks of unequal density. Since density or specific weight is a property common to all rock types regardless of origin, this instrument can detect irregularities in the structure and composition of sedimentary as well as basement rocks.

A different way of covering the largest number of square kilometers in the shortest time and at very reasonable cost is the geological interpretation of **aerial photographs.**

In areas where the bedrock is not obscured by tropical vegetation, glacial till, water or ice, a **photogeologist** can determine the thickness, the structure, and often the gross lithology (sandstone, limestone, shale) of outcropping formations. Even if the surface strata are seemingly featureless it is often possible to make slight deviations from the regional tilt visible by mapping so-called **drainage anomalies.** Running water is extremely sensitive to the most minute changes in elevation. Rivers and creeks follow slopes and circumvent rises that would otherwise go unnoticed.

Exploring for Structural Traps

Structure is still a magic word in the oil patch. Everybody likes structural prospects. Executives and shareholders can understand them, engineers can define them, they keep geophysicists in business, and for geologists they are easy to sell.

While anticlines and faults can, under favorable conditions, be mapped on the ground or from the air, normally they are without surface expression and must be tracked down the hard way, by subsurface geology and geophysics.

Once the exploration of a basin has progressed beyond the initial stage and some drilling has been done, the subsurface geologist takes over. His stock in trade is information gleaned from measurements and observations on the surface and in boreholes, information about the depth, thickness, age, sequence, composition, porosity and fluid content of the penetrated strata.

Structure Contour Maps

The most important properties of an oil-bearing formation are its shape and orientation in space. These properties are portrayed by structure contour maps.

Subsurface structure maps are based on the same principle as topographic contour maps. But where the land surveyor can achieve any desired degree of accuracy by simply tightening his network of survey stations, his groping counterpart has only a limited number of control points. What happens beween boreholes is anybody's guess, and the viewer of a subsurface map, unless he is an expert in his own right, is at the mercy of the mapmaker. The conclusions drawn from a given set

Figure XV-9 — Seismic crewman lays geophone line on Ellef Ringnes Island in the Canadian Arctic.

of figures separate the explorer from the wishful thinker, the oil-finder from the prospect-peddler, and considered opinion from geopoetry.

The best subsurface structure map has its limitations. It can lead directly to a drillable location, but more often it is just a work sheet on which to plot a more penetrating geophysical investigation.

Seismic Shooting

The vast majority of structural oil and gas fields around the world have been found by the **reflection seismograph.**

The seismic method is based on the same principle as the echo sounder. The time elapsed between a signal and the return of its echo is a measure of the distance of the reflecting object. Instead of a sound the exploration seismologist sets off a shock wave, either by blasting ("shooting") or by dropping a heavy weight, and hopes that the wave will be reflected by rock surfaces several hundreds of metres below (Fig.

XV-9). This process, repeated at closely spaced shotpoints could, under ideal conditions result in a map on which the arrival time of shock waves from a subsurface reflector horizon are plotted and contoured to resemble a detailed structure contour map. But ideal conditions never exist.

First of all, the velocity with which a shock wave travels through the earth differs not only from shale to sandstone and from sandstone to limestone, but also from area to area within the same rock type. Therefore, arrival times are ambiguous, and it is often difficult to correlate recorded reflections with known geological boundaries.

Secondly, the average geological section has more than one or two potential reflectors. Any interface of rocks with sufficiently different acoustic or elastic properties qualifies, and this compounds the problem of reflection identification.

The exploration seismologist is a precision-minded professional in a highly developed, competitive field. He uses delicate instruments and sophisticated techniques. Only one link in his otherwise near-perfect system is of unknown dimension and questionable workmanship, and that is his energy conductor, the rock column between shotpoint and reflector.

The seismic method works best where the subsurface formations are arranged in neat layers, where their sequence is undisturbed by erosional intervals, and where structures are prominent. But, it remains the most important geophysical exploration tool.

Exploring for Stratigraphic Traps

In nature and the minds of man, stratigraphic traps have a low profile. Anticlines and fault structures are less obscure and easier to understand, but their discovery is no more pressing. True, many fields owe their existence to a combination of stratigraphic and structural factors, but in these cases structure usually serves merely to localize oil or gas accumulations along a stratigraphic trend. The trend must be found first.

Of the many ways in which primary and secondary stratigraphic trends are mapped, only the most common can be introduced here.

Isopach and Facies Maps

The earth is not a solid ball of rock. A sedimentary basin is not a stable fixture; its ups and downs are reflected, as a rule, by the thickening and thinning of the basin fill.

Most petroleum originates in marine shales in the deep basin from where it migrates into the sandstones and reef carbonates of the shallow rims and platforms. It is, therefore, imperative to chart the thicknesses of selected sedimentary bodies. The resulting maps are called **isopach maps.**

The variable composition (facies) of a rock unit, its change from sand to shale or from limestone to dolomite can be shown on **facies maps.**

Facies and thickness trends often coincide, and one map can complement the other in projecting a known string of stratigraphic traps into new prospective areas.

CHAPTER XVII

Drilling for Oil and Gas

The Right to Drill

The best geological prospect is useless if it cannot be tested. Before an oil company can place a rig in the chosen location, it must secure the **oil and gas rights.** Then, the authorities must grant permission to drill, and finally the landowner must be compensated for the inevitable temporary damage to roads, soil and vegetation, and for the annoyance. While the two latter conditions are generally a matter of routine application and negotiation, to acquire oil and gas rights is more difficult and much more costly.

Oil and Gas Rights

Originally, surface and mineral rights went together. Only from 1887 on did the Government of Canada exclude all mines and minerals from homesteads granted west of the Third Meridian (106° West, just west of Moose Jaw, Saskatchewan), and after 1889 mineral rights were withheld from Crown patents east of the Third. In 1930, the federal government transferred all Crown lands, mines, minerals and royalties (except Indian reservations, national parks and Veterans Land Administration property) to the provinces.

The direct way of obtaining oil and gas rights (or "land" in industry parlance) is by **sealed bidding.** Company A, wishing to drill on a certain undisposed parcel may apply for the posting of the land in question at one of the sales held more or less regularly in the oil-producing provinces.

Where the rights to the desirable target are held by Company B (perhaps by virtue of outbidding Company A at the sale), Company B can be approached with a **farmout** proposal. The resulting agreement most likely provides for the drilling of a well at the expense of Company A, the **farmee,** and the sharing of the production (if any) with Company B, the **farmor.**

Townships and Ranges

In 1871, the **township** was established as the basic land survey unit in the Canadian prairies. It measures 6 by 6 miles and is divided into 36 **sections** of 1 square mile (640 acres) each (Figure XVI-1). Townships are numbered northward from the U.S. border. Rows or **"ranges"** of townships are numbered from east to west, beginning at principal meridians, the first of which runs through Fort Gary, Manitoba. The Second, Third, Fourth, Fifth and Sixth Meridian coincide with 102°, 106°, 110° (the Alberta-Saskatchewan border), 114°, and 118° West. As an

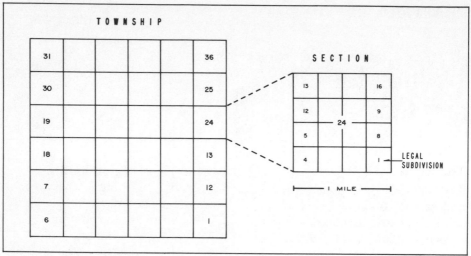

Figure XVI-1 — Townships, Sections and Legal Subdivisions are the basic land survey units in Western Canada.

example, Township 2, Range 2 west of the Fourth Meridian (or Tp.2, Rg.2W4M in short) lies 6 miles west of the Alberta-Saskatchewan, and 6 miles north of the American border.

In Canada, sections are numbered from the southeast corner of each township. They are subdivided into 16 **Legal Subdivisions** (LSDs), also numbered from the southeast corner of the section.

These, then, are the terms in which a drilling location in Western Canada is described. Shell Manyberries 14-21-5-5W4 was drilled in LSD 14, Sec. 21, Tp.5, Rg.5 west of the Fourth Meridian in the southeast corner of Alberta.

Drilling the Wildcat:

Rotary Drilling

Modern oil wells (Figure XVI-2) are drilled by the rotary method. A cutting **bit** at the end of a string of hollow **drill pipe** is rotated into the ground. The rock **cuttings** are cleared away by a stream of specially prepared **drilling fluid** or **"mud"**, which is pumped down the pipe and up again through the borehole. The mud stream lubricates and cools the rotary bit, carries geologically diagnostic rock chips or **samples** to the surface, and keeps the walls of the hole from caving in by lining them with a protective **mud cake.** The weight of the mud column also controls the formation pressure whenever an oil- or gas-bearing zone is tapped.

Should the well start "kicking" in spite of good mud control, a **blowout preventer** (BOP) attached to the wellhead in a cellar below the rig floor can be closed at a moment's notice. Wild "gushers" as proud signals of discovery are a thing of the past.

Normally, the drill bit is expected to go straight down, but there are cases where a well must be drilled **directionally.** This is desirable, for example, when the rig cannot be placed exactly over the subsurface objective, or when a piece of

Figure XVI-2 — A drilling rig in the Alberta Foothills. (Courtesy Nabors Drilling Limited, Calgary.)

equipment, a "fish", is irretrievably lost in the hole and must now be sidetracked. Until recently, steel wedges, so-called **whipstocks** were inserted to guide the bit in a predetermined direction. Today, operators use a drill bit driven by a **down-hole motor** and mounted on a piece of slightly angled pipe, the **bent sub.**

The deviation of a directionally drilled well can be controlled precisely enough to hit a geological target 3,000 meters down and 1,500 meters off to the side, or to squeeze water from a **relief well** into a borehole of a well burning 100 meters away.

A whole arsenal of equipment is

Figure XVI-3 — Roughnecks change drill bit.

necessary to make all this possible. There is the familiar drilling **derrick** or **mast** and its substructure, there are **draw works** and engines to hoist and rotate the drill pipe, **pumps** and containers for the mud system, water and fuel **tanks,** an **electric plant,** and stacks of drill pipe. There are also trailers for the **"tool push"** (the master of the rig) and the wellsite geologist.

A 24-Hour Job

Once started, drilling continues round-the-clock in 8-hour shifts. Each of the three crews consists of a foreman or **driller,** a senior **derrickman,** three or four **floormen,** and a **motorman.** If the location is remote without a nearby town for crew accommodation, a complete camp is provided at the drillsite.

In most parts of Canada the drill cuts through unconsolidated glacial drift before it hits bedrock. Should a loose rock fall into the hole when it is deeper, it could jam the drill pipe and cause costly repairs. Therefore, and to prevent the contamination of shallow freshwater sources, the authorities stipulate that **surface casing** be set as soon as bedrock is reached.

In a typical 1,500 to 2,000 m (4,920 to 6,560 ft.) well in central Alberta, the procedure is to drill a 12¼-inch surface hole to the prescribed depth, say 200 m (656 ft.), run 8⅝-inch casing, and fill the space between rock and pipe with cement. (Drill pipe and casing are manufactured to the specifications of the American Petroleum Institute (API) and it may take a while until their dimensions are given in metric units.)

When the cement is dry, after 24 hours or so, drilling continues with a 7⅞-inch bit. At first, water is as good a drilling fluid as any, but it must be changed to proper mud before potentially oil- or gas-bearing zones are reached. Only a carefully concocted mixture of fluids, solids and chemicals can perform all its control and transport functions without damaging prospective formations by clogging their pore spaces. This is so important that the design and supervision of mud programs, and the supply of the required additives are left to special service companies.

Checking the Formation

Throughout the drilling operation rock cuttings carried to the surface in the mud stream are washed, dried and examined under the microscope. These chips are small, about 32 mm (⅛ inch) in diameter, and it is never certain whether they come from the bottom of the hole or from its sides. Therefore, when he needs more reliable information about the age and nature of a formation, the wellsite geologist can call for a **core.**

The drill pipe is pulled, the cutting bit replaced by a hollow **core barrel** with a ring-type diamond-studded bit, and the whole assembly is lowered to the bottom again. Sixty feet (the length of the core barrel) later, the coring tool is pulled, the core carefully extracted and washed and stored in boxes for detailed inspection.

Since the temporary changeover to coring equipment takes extra rig

Figure XVI-4 — Part of an electric well log in central Alberta, showing the Cretaceous/Devonian unconformity.

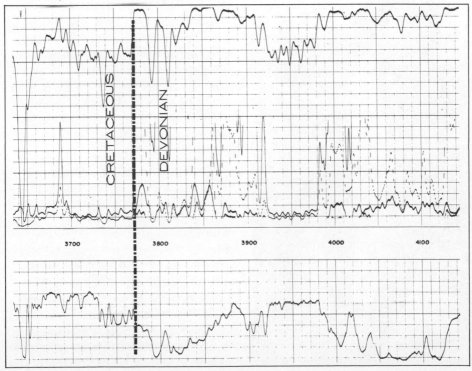

time, coring is expensive and justified only if it helps to solve geological problems or yields indispensible data for reservoir studies.

As soon as the bit reaches **total depth** (T.D.) the well is logged. **Well logging** is the continuous recording by downhole instruments of the electrical, radioactive, acoustic and other properties of the penetrated formations. A **sonde** is lowered to the bottom of the borehole at the end of a wireline, and as it is slowly raised at a constant speed, its readings are transmitted to the logging truck and recorded on graph paper (Figure XVI-4). The properties measured, singly or in combination, can be interpreted in terms of lithology, porosity and fluid content. The characteristic configuration of the recorded curves is a means of correlating subsurface formations over long distances.

Prospective zones can be **tested** on the way down, i.e. as soon as a porous formation is breached and shows of oil or gas appear in the drilling mud. The testing tool, a perforated chamber containing a pressure recording device, is attached to the drill pipe and sent to the bottom. The formation to be tested and the recording chamber are then isolated from the rest of the hole by activating an expandable rubber **packer** included in the test assembly. The recorder measures the changing pressures exerted by the formation fluid under shut-in and flow conditions and thereby provides information about the productivity of the zone in question.

If the tested interval contains gas, it usually blows to the surface under its own pressure. If the formation fluid is oil or water or both, a sample returns with the drill pipe when it is pulled. If the formation is tighter than expected, only a few litres of mud may drain from the pipe as the tool is removed.

The operator can complete the entire drilling operation and wait for the logs to be examined before tests are taken. The procedure is the same, except that a bottom packer is added to the test assembly so that the hole both above and below the zone to be investigated can be sealed off.

If the tests yield nothing but mud, water, or hydrocarbons in non-commercial quantities, and if the verdict of the log analyst is discouraging, the well is **plugged.**

Vertical fluid communication within the subsurface and between it and the atmosphere could contaminate water sources. It could also waste formation pressure which may be needed elsewhere to drive petroleum into another borehole. Therefore, the authorities charged with oil and gas conservation require that all porous formations be sealed with cement plugs before the rig is released.

The status of the well is now D&A, **dry and abandoned.**

Completing the Discovery

Complete or abandon — not always an easy question to answer. The results of tests and log interpretation are, sometimes, inconclusive, and the cost of completing can approach that of drilling a hole.

A well to be placed on production must first be cased to prevent it from caving in and to facilitate a variety of completion, production and maintenance operations.

In a typical central Alberta location with a surface hole already lined with 8⅝-inch pipe, a string of 4½-inch **production casing** is placed in the well. Cement pumped down the pipe and up the **annulus,** the space between pipe and rock, secures the casing in the hole and isolates the porous zones from each other to keep the subsurface pressure regime intact.

When the production casing is in place, the drilling rig is released and a light **service rig** or truck-mounted winch takes over.

In certain hard and stable reservoir rocks, wells can be completed "open hole" or "barefoot", with the **casing shoe** landed at the top of the producing formation, but usually the casing goes down to T.D. and is then perforated.

The **perforating gun,** a device suspended at the end of a wireline, fires broadsides of bullets or shaped charges through the casing and the surrounding cement into the formation. This method allows the owner of the well to open only that part of the producing formation which will give the best results. In the case of an oil completion, for instance, perforations can be placed so that neither water from below nor gas from the top of the pool can enter the well in quantity.

There are few wells whose performance will not benefit from some kind of **stimulation.** In limestones and dolomites, hydrochloric **acid** will increase the permeability. The flow resistance in sandstones can be partly overcome by hydraulic **fracturing.** This is the technique of pumping a sand-laden fluid into the formation under sufficiently high pressure to open cracks through which the oil can flow into the well. The sand serves to prop the fractures open when the pressure subsides.

Figure XVI-5 — On man-made island in the Beaufort Sea, Imperial's Sarpik well explores for oil.

Figure XVI-6 — Semi-submersible drilling platform on the Canadian east coast.

Before the well can be placed on production another string of pipe, the **tubing,** may have to be installed. Practically all crude oils and some gases contain varying amounts of corrosive impurities, such as salt and sulphur. Being firmly cemented into the borehole, the casing must last through the life of the well. Tubing, on the other hand, can be pulled, inspected, and exchanged if necessary. Another reason for using removable production pipe is that its diameter can be changed several times in response to the declining energy of the pool. The smaller the diameter, the less pressure is needed at the bottom to lift the oil column. If oil has to be raised by pumping, oversized down-hole and surface equipment would be required to produce through the casing.

Figure XVI-7 — Drillship in the Beaufort Sea. (Courtesy Dome Petroleum Limited, Calgary.)

Offshore Drilling

Drilling offshore is basically the same as drilling on land. It can be done from fixed or floating platforms.

The simplest way of supporting a rig offshore is by dredging up a small **man-made island,** a method employed in the shallowest parts of the Beaufort Sea (Figure XVI-5).

More commonly, **fixed platforms** are steel structures resting on the sea floor, with a working deck at least 15 m (49 ft.) above mean sea level. They are best suited for the directional drilling of up to 40 field development (as opposed to wildcat) wells from the same surface location.

The **jackup platform** combines mobility and stability (Figure XVI-

6). It is either towed or it moves to the wellsite under its own steam. Its 4 or 6 legs are lowered to the sea floor, sometimes over 100 m (330 ft.), and then used to jack the platform up out of reach of the waves.

When towed, **semi-submersible platforms** float high above the water on three or more huge vertical or two horizontal cylinders. When ballasted at the drill site, the floats are allowed to sink to a level where they are more or less below wave base. Simultaneously, this takes the platform down to the working position.

The lateral stability of the semi-submersible is maintained by anchors. To compensate for unavoidable vertical movements, rig and sea floor are connected by a flexible, telescoping hollow **riser** through which the drill pipe is lowered and raised. Wellhead and blowout preventers are installed at the bottom.

Semi-submersibles can drill with their floats resting on the sea bed or in waters several hundred metres deep.

In northern waters infested by drifting ice, fixed or sluggish steel platforms are out of the question. This is why wildcats in the deeper Beaufort Sea and on the Labrador Shelf are drilled exclusively from ships, which can retreat from the drill site within minutes if necessary.

The **drillship** (Figure XVI-7) has a hole, the **moon-pool** in the bottom through which the drill pipe runs. Again, a marine conductor or riser connects the rig with the wellhead at the sea floor.

Drillships can either be moored to the sea bed or **dynamically positioned** by computer- and beacon-controlled **thrusters.** They can operate in waters of over 1000 meters (3,300 ft.).

A special kind of drilling platform has been successfully tested in the sheltered waters between the Canadian Arctic Islands, where movements of the ice cover are at a minimum. It is created by pumping water onto, and thereby **strengthening the ice** itself in the selected location as a safe foundation for heavy drilling equipment.

CHAPTER XVIII

Gas and Oil from Well to Market

Production

Producible gas will always flow to the surface, and many oil pools have enough initial **reservoir energy** to send their contents up through the tubing unassisted. Wells that can be expected to flow for some time to come produce through a **"christmas tree"**, a wellhead assembly of control valves and gauges (Figure XVII-1).

If the reservoir pressure is too low from the beginning, or if it drops during the productive history of the well, oil must be lifted by **pump.** The oscillating **walking beam,** connected by a string of **sucker rods** with the downhole **plunger** is a familiar sight in oil-producing areas (Figure XVII-2).

Oil that is clean enough can go directly into **flow lines** and **tanks** from where it is trucked or piped to the nearest **gathering station.** For wells flowing under gas drive, surface installations include one or more steel vessels for the step-by-step reduction of the wellhead pressure and the accompanying **separation** of the gas from the oil. In pumping wells the oil is often mixed with salt water and a **treater** is installed to break the emulsion with heat and chemicals.

Reservoir Energy

Petroleum engineers charged with making the most economical use of the natural energy of a reservoir have their own way of looking at an oil or gas pool. They don't care whether it occurs as a result of a structural or stratigraphic accident, they want to know what drives the hydrocarbons into the wells.

There are **water drive** fields where the **hydrostatic head** of an underlying water column supplies the push. As long as the petroleum is not produced at an excessive rate, the rising water level will keep the reservoir pressurized. Sooner or later the downdip edge wells will "go to water", but the higher ones will continue to produce until all recoverable oil has been withdrawn. If the natural water drive does not provide enough energy, pressure can be maintained artificially by converting strategically located wells from producers to water **injectors.** Under water drive up to 75% of the "oil in place" is recoverable.

In **solution-gas** pools the oil is propelled by dissolved gas. As the reservoir pressure is reduced by production, gas expands and tends to bubble out of solution. It seeks its way to the nearest well, dragging a

Figure XVII-1 — Gas is brought to the surface in a similar manner to oil, except that it never has to be pumped. The flow is controlled by a "Christmas tree" such as this one in the Waterton gas field, Alberta.

certain amount of oil along with it. But since this type of drive does not have the broad-front sweeping action of a water drive, it is more difficult to control and the reservoir energy drops more rapidly. Up to 90% of the oil in place may remain there unless **secondary pressure maintenance** measures like gas- or water-injection are taken.

Transportation

People and petroleum rarely accumulate in the same place. Los Angeles is an exception. Crude oil for Japan comes from Indonesia, propane for New York from Texas; Algeria keeps Paris warm, and Venezuela supplies Halifax.

Pipelines

Pipelines are the safest and most efficient medium for the bulk transportation of gas, oil and petroleum products. They come in diameters up to 142 cm (56 inches) and lengths of thousands of kilometres. They can be laid in just about any terrain and even under water and ice.

Crude oil pipelines are designed to take raw oil from producing fields or from tanker terminals to refineries. One of the longest in the world connects Edmonton, Alberta, with Montreal, Quebec.

Products pipelines carry refinery products to petrochemical plants. Different products such as naphtha, kerosene and gasoline can be pumped through the same multi-product line as long as they are sent on their way in batches and at rates fast enough to prevent intermingling.

Gas pipelines fall in two categories. From producing to market areas, often over very long distances, gas is transported in large-diameter **transmission** lines. Small-diameter **distribution** lines are laid by local utility companies to take gas from the transmission terminal to the consumer.

Pipeline Construction

Before a pipeline can be built, the **right-of-way** must be acquired from all landowners along the projected route. After clearing and grading a strip of land wide enough for the pipe itself and the heavy construction equipment, the line can be laid on, in or above the ground.

In warm climates pipelines may be placed **on the ground.** In North America they are usually buried, not only to protect them from temperature changes and surface traffic, but also to restore the land to its former condition.

Figure XVII-2 — An oil pump. The wellhead is on the left.

Arctic pipeline construction differs somewhat from that in moderate zones. More than half of the 1292 km (801 mi.) trans-Alaska (Alyeska) crude oil line, for example, was heavily insulated and laid on **elevated** crossbeams in order not to disturb the permafrost and to minimize the risk of earthquake damage.

Usually, however, a **trench** deep enough to cover the line with about 1 m (3.3 ft.) of earth is dug and the pipes are strung out alongside. They are **welded** into a continuous line, **coated** with bituminous enamel, **wrapped** in fibreglass tape, and lowered into the ditch (Figure XVII-3). The entire operation from trenching to backfilling is an integrated, highly mechanized line-travelling process. When it is completed and **pumps** have been installed at strategic intervals along the route, the line is **pressure-tested** before it is filled with oil, gas, or products.

Figure XVII-3 — Pipeline construction. Lengths of pipe are strung out on the right-of-way, ready to be welded together, while the ditch in which the pipeline is to be buried is being dug.

Tankers

Although subsea pipelines like those from the producing fields in the North Sea to the surrounding countries are practical and will become more common as offshore exploration moves into deeper waters, the long-haul international oil trade relies on the tanker.

Tankers are designed for specific purposes. Some carry petroleum products across the Great Lakes, others take liquefied gas from Algeria to the eastern seaboard of the United States, and supertankers with crude oil from the Persian Gulf supply refineries in Japan and California.

A modern tanker is a ship whose **superstructure** (navigation bridge, stores, shops, living quarters, etc.) and **engine rooms** are located **aft** to leave the central and forward portions of the vessel free for maintenance, safety and cargo-handling facilities on the **weather deck,** and for **tanks** and **pump rooms** below (Figure XVII-4).

In contrast to most dry-cargo freighters, which take on goods at both ends of the journey, tankers on the return trip from discharge to loading port must be ballasted with sea water to remain seaworthy. **Ballast** can be carried in special compartments or in cargo tanks.

The largest tankers have a carrying capacity of 540,000 dwt **(deadweight tons),** and even ordinary supertankers of only half that size are 335 m (1,100 ft.) long and draw 21 m (69 ft.) of water. Conventional harbours have no docking facilities for them, and supertankers are, therefore, loaded and unloaded at special **offshore terminals** with pipeline connections to shore-based holding tanks.

Navigating an oil tanker is no more difficult than navigating other seagoing ships, but large tankers are much less manoeuverable than coastal freighters. If they collide or run aground, the environmental damage can be large and lasting.

Rail and Road

Over long distances, crude oil is transported by pipelines, but petroleum products in large quantities are regularly carried by rail **tank cars.**

Figure XVII-4 — A helicopter drops supplies and mail onto deck of "Marisa", 206,937 dwt, as she passes 12 miles off the Cape of Good Hope, South Africa, with a cargo of crude oil for Europe.

Trucking plays a major role in oil field transport, including the hauling of crude oil from small fields or isolated wells to the nearest gathering station. Large tanker trucks designed to take petroleum products from refineries to petrochemical plants, wholesalers or consumers are a familiar sight on all highways.

Refining and Marketing

Broken down into elements, **crude oil** is a mixture of carbon (84-87% in weight), hydrogen (11-14%), sulphur (1-8%), nitrogen (0.1-1.7%), oxygen (0.5%) and traces of iron, vanadium, nickel and a few other metals. As produced from the subsurface it is almost always contaminated by water, inorganic matter or gas. In its appearance it ranges from highly mobile and light brown to highly viscous and black. The odor of some oils is not unpleasant, but others smell like rotten eggs with garlic.

Most of the watery, gaseous and solid impurities are removed in wellsite **separators** before the crude is allowed into the pipeline. The oil supplied to the **refinery** (Fig. 18) consists of hydrocarbon and other organic compounds involving the remaining elements listed above. It is the job of the **refinery engineer** not only to **separate** the more or less volatile hydrocarbons from each other, but to **convert** certain less desirable compounds into commercially more valuable ones.

Figure XVII-5 — An oil refinery at Montreal East.

The different hydrocarbons of a crude oil have different **boiling points;** they can be sorted into groups of petroleum products, such as gasoline, kerosene, lubricating oil and fuel oil by **distillation.**

Unfortunately, the products resulting from this first refinery process do not come in the ratios and qualities required. There is, for instance, more demand for gasoline than kerosene, and the gasoline produced by distillation is not good enough for modern engines.

Among the more important processes devised by refiners to transform surplus into choice molecules are **cracking, reforming, polymerisation, alkylation** and **isomerisation,** all designed to rearrange the atoms of

the treated hydrocarbon compounds by heat and pressure in or without the presence of suitable chemical agents (catalysts).

Finished refinery products are **propane** and **butane** (gases that are transported and sold in condensed form as LPGs, liquefied petroleum gases), **motor** and **aviation gasoline, jet fuel, diesel oil, heating oil, lubricants, waxes** and **asphalt,** all marketed in the familiar manner through wholesale and retail outlets.

Certain intermediate, unfinished refinery products are sold to petrochemical plants as **feedstocks** for the manufacture of plastics, resins, synthetic fibres, fertilizers, pesticides, cleaning agents and other consumer goods.

CHAPTER XIX

Finding Out More

It is hoped that the reader who has absorbed the preceding chapters, will have gained something in the way of a fundamental knowledge of the general workings of the mineral industry, and of what makes it go. It is also hoped that he will be enabled to read public reports of mining and oil activities at least partly relieved of the sense of mystery which had formerly seemed to enshroud them. If the book has done its work at all well, it is possible that some readers will have had their curiosity aroused to the level at which they may well ask, "tell me more", and to such this chapter is addressed.

In the first place, it should be cautioned that these industries, embracing as they do all the processes from geological reconnaissance through to finished metals, or petroleum products are fields which are professionally served by many kinds of experts at many points in the broad spectrum they present. It is thus impossible to create through self-study alone, anything like an expertise in any branch, let alone the whole technology. We can, however, suggest to the reader various means and sources whereby his curiosity may become somewhat satisfied — though it would still have to fall short of the point of having "everyone his own mineral or petroleum engineer".

There are a number of technical societies, most with several highly developed, specialized divisions serving the operators, researchers, and the administrators of the many units making up the Canadian mineral industries. In addition, there are many foreign societies who number Canadians among their membership, and this in itself suggests a large and growing body of highly technical literature.

Prospectors' Classes

One excellent service which is provided by the various mining provinces of Canada, is offered in classes for prospectors, and these are organized by the Department of Mines of the various provinces. Any interested person may enrol for these, and attend lectures, seminars, and demonstrations in geology, mineralogy, and prospecting methods. The classes are held in the late winter or early spring months, and are usually on an itinerant circuit so that they are available at some time or another at several of the major centres of population, as well as in the principal mining areas. A letter to the local provincial Department of Mines or Natural Resources, as the case may be, will elicit the desired information. In Vancouver, the British Columbia and Yukon Chamber of Mines has for many years sponsored a popular prospectors' course.

Oil exploration is a multi-million dollar business and does not lend itself to individual effort.

Plant Visits

In general, visits to underground workings are not available to casual visitors. Some of the larger mines and oil refining companies do, however, organize tours of surface plants, and have on hand well-prepared information for the layman. Those who may be taking a motor holiday which may include a mineral producing area, could perhaps benefit from advice which is usually available with the local provincial department or bureau of tourism. There are modest mining museums at Cobalt, Ont., and Britannia Beach, B.C., for instance.

Geological Surveys

In earlier chapters, reference has been made to the activities of the geological surveys conducted by the Federal and Provincial governments. These agencies publish hundreds of reports each year on many aspects of regional, local, and economic geology, as well as many kinds of maps, all of which are available for purchase. As this material is produced, the items are noted in the periodical literature, together with prices and places of availability.

Of these, the publications of the Geological Survey of Canada may be found in, or may be ordered through, the bookshops in the larger cities and towns which specialize in governmental publications. Similarly, the provinces with Departments of Mines, or their local counterparts, publish geological reports and maps, and these are available from the department concerned.

The petroleum and gas activities of the Geological Survey of Canada are directed from the Institute of Sedimentary and Petroleum Geology, 3300, 33rd Street, N.W., Calgary, Alberta T2L 2A7.

In addition to geological literature referred to, the Canadian Centre for Mineral & Energy Technology, Department of Energy, Mines and Resources, Ottawa K1A 0G1 publishes a great many reports on individual mineral commodities and their technology and processing. As well as metals, these include reports on fuels, oil and gas technology, refining and transportation.

General Reading

The following list contains good, readable, and often enjoyable material for those who wish to seek further knowledge. Most of the titles are available at the better reference libraries, and usually in the public libraries in mining centres.

MINING:

"Prospecting in Canada" by A. H. Lang, Economic Geology Report No. 7, Geological Survey of Canada, Ottawa, Ont. K1A 0E8.

"Geology and Economic Minerals of Canada" (2 vols.). Edited by C. H. Stockwell. Economic Geology Report No. 1, Geological Survey of Canada, Ottawa, Ont. K1A 0E8.

"Canadian Minerals Yearbook", Mineral Policy Sector, Department of Energy, Mines and Resources, Ottawa, Ont. K1A 0E4.

"Canadian Mines Handbook" Northern Miner Press Ltd., 7 Labatt Ave., Toronto M5A 3P2.

"How to Read Financial Statements", Canadian Securities Institute, P.O. Box 225, Commerce Court South, Toronto M5L 1E8.

"What Mining Means to Canada", and "The Modern Miner", Mining Association of Canada, 350 Sparks St., Suite 705, Ottawa, Ont. K1R 7S8.

"Man and Metals" by T. A. Rickard, McGraw-Hill.

"Romance of Mining" by T. A. Rickard, McGraw-Hill.

"Diamond Drill Handbook" by J. D. Cumming. J. K. Smit & Sons of Canada Ltd., 81 Tycos Drive, Toronto M6B 1W5.

"Mining in Canada", Canadian Institute of Mining & Metallurgy, 1130 Sherbrooke St. W., Montreal H3A 2M8.

"Out of the Earth" by G. B. Langford, University of Toronto Press.

ENERGY RESOURCES:

"Energy in Canada — an Overview", Department of Energy, Mines and Resources, Ottawa, Ont. K1A 0E4.

"Canadian Oil Supply and Requirements", National Energy Board, Ottawa, Ont. K1A 0E5.

"Statistical Yearbook", Canadian Petroleum Association, 1500, 633-6 Avenue S.W., Calgary, Alberta, T2P 2Y5.

"Oil Sands and Heavy Oils: the Prospects", Department of Energy, Mines and Resources, Ottawa, Ont. K1A 0E4.

"1976 Assessment of Canada's Coal Reserves and Resources", Department of Energy, Mines and Resources, Ottawa, Ont. K1A 0E4.

"Oil and Natural Gas Industries of Canada 1978", Department of Energy, Mines and Resources, Ottawa, Ont. K1A 0E4.

"Oil and Natural Gas Reserves of Canada 1976", Department of Energy, Mines and Resources, Ottawa, Ont. K1A 0E4.

"Canadian Coal Industry Report", Northern Miner Press Ltd., 7 Labatt Ave., Toronto M5A 3P2

"Introduction to Energy in Canada", Department of Energy, Mines and Resources, Ottawa, Ont. K1A 0E4.

"Coal in Canada", Department of Energy, Mines and Resources, Ottawa, Ont. K1A 0E4.

"Our Industry — Petroleum", published by British Petroleum Company, available from BP's PR Department, 1245 Sherbrooke St. W., Montreal, Que. H3G 1J7.

"Modern Petroleum — A Basic Primer of the Industry", by Bill Berger and Ken Anderson, Petroleum Publishing Company, P.O. Box 1260, Tulsa, Oklahoma 74101.

"Environmental Protection and the Petroleum Industry", Petroleum Association for Conservation of the Canadian Environment, Suite 400, 130 Albert Street, Ottawa, Ontario K1P 5G4.

"Oil and Gas in Alberta", Canadian Petroleum Association, 1500, 633-6 Avenue S.W., Calgary, Alberta T2P 2Y5.

"The Natural Gas Story", Canadian Gas Association, 55 Scarsdale Road, Don Mills, Ontario M3B 2R3.

The associations mentioned above, as well as The Arctic Petroleum Operators' Association, P.O. Box 1281, Postal Station M, Calgary, Alberta T2P 2J2, provide various publications of a general and technical nature. In addition, most of the major oil companies have available a selection of literature on the oil and gas industries. Among these are: Public Affairs Department, Gulf Canada Ltd., 800 Bay St., Toronto, Ontario M5S 1Y8, which also has an extensive film library; Imperial Oil Ltd., P.O. Box 4029, Terminal A, Toronto, Ontario M5W 1K3; Shell Canada Ltd., P.O. Box 400, Terminal A, Toronto, Ontario M5W 1E1.

Periodical Literature

In regard to the technology of the world of mining and the oil and gas industries, the greatest body lies in periodical technical publications. Of these, the proceedings and bulletins of the specialized technical societies are available only to their memberships. There are however several good monthly magazines published by independent periodical publishing houses, and these contain a good balance of the technical, general, historic and business data.

CHAPTER XX

Common Mining, Oil and Financial Terms

Mining Terms

ACID ROCK — Usually refers to an igneous rock carrying a high proportion of silica.

ADIT — A passageway or opening driven horizontally into the side of a hill generally for the purpose of exploring or otherwise opening a mineral deposit. Strictly, an adit is open to the atmosphere at one end, a tunnel at both ends.

AERIAL SURVEY — A survey made from an aircraft to obtain photographs, or measure magnetic properties, radioactivity, etc.

AERIAL TRAMWAY — A system for the transporting of ore or rock in buckets which are suspended from a cable.

AGITATION — In metallurgy, the act or state of being stirred or shaken mechanically, sometimes accompanied by the introduction of compressed air.

AIR BLAST — A colloquialism. More correctly known as a rock burst *(See)*.

ALLOY — A compound of two or more metals, usually produced by fusion.

ALLUVIAL, ALLUVIUM — Deposits of sedimentary material laid down in river beds, flood plains, lakes, or at the foot of mountain slopes.

ALTERATION — Any physical or chemical change in a rock or mineral subsequent to its formation.

AMALGAM — An alloy of mercury with another metal.

AMALGAMATION — A process by which gold and silver are extracted from an ore by dissolving them in mercury.

AMORPHOUS — A term applied to rocks or minerals that possess no definite crystal structure or form.

ANODE — A rectangular plate of copper (or other metal) cast in a shape suitable for refining by the electrolytic process.

ANOMALY — A term applied to a departure from the normal or field characteristic, commonly used in geophysical prospecting. Thus, in a magnetometer survey an area showing much higher (or much lower) readings of magnetic intensity than the surrounding area would be identified as an anomaly.

ANTICLINE — An arch or fold in the layers of rock shaped like the crest of a wave, as opposed to a syncline which is similar to the trough of a wave.

APEX — The top or terminal edge of a vein on surface or its nearest point to the surface.

AREAL MAP — A geologic map showing the area or extent of the different rocks exposed at surface.

ASSAY — To test ores or minerals by chemical or other methods for the purpose of determining the amount of valuable metals contained.

ASSAY FOOT (INCH, CM) — The assay value multiplied by the number of feet (inches, centimetres) across which the sample is taken.

ASSESSMENT WORK — The amount of work specified by law, which must be done each year to retain legal control of mining lands.

AUTOGENOUS GRINDING — The process of grinding in a rotating mill which uses as a grinding medium large pieces or pebbles of the ore being ground, instead of conventional steel balls or rods.

BACK — The ceiling of a drift, crosscut or stope.

BACKGROUND — The minor radioactivity shown by a counter which is not due to abnormal amounts of radioactive minerals nearby. The background is accounted for by cosmic rays and the minor residual radioactivity in the vicinity.

BACKSTOPE — The initial lift or slice when commencing to stope or mine from a drift.

BALL MILL — A cylindrical shaped steel container filled with steel balls into which crushed ore is fed. The ball mill is rotated, causing the balls to cascade, which in turn grinds the ore.

BANDED ORE (STRUCTURE) — Composed of bands or layers of minerals (rocks) differing in color and texture.

BASEMENT ROCKS — The underlying or older rock mass. Often refers to rocks of Precambrian age which may be covered by later rocks.

BASE METAL — A metal inferior in value to gold and silver, generally applied to the industrial metals such as copper, lead, etc.

BASIC ROCK — An igneous rock, relatively low in silica and composed mostly of dark-colored minerals.

BATHOLITH — A large mass of igneous rock extending to great depth and with its upper portion dome-like in shape. It has crystallized below surface, but may be exposed due to erosion of the overlying rock. Smaller masses of igneous rocks are known as bosses or plugs.

BEDROCK — Solid rock forming the earth's crust, frequently covered by soil or water.

BENEFICIATE — To concentrate or enrich; e.g., as applied to the preparation of iron ore for smelting, through such processes as sintering, magnetic concentration, washing, etc.

BENTONITE — A clay which has great ability to absorb water and swells accordingly.

BIOLOGICAL LEACHING – A process for recovering metals from low grade ores by dissolving them in solution, the dissolution being aided by bacterial action.

BIT – The cutting end of a boring instrument. In rock drilling, it is frequently made with ultra-hard material such as diamonds or tungsten carbide.

BLACK JACK – A miner's term for sphalerite or zinc blende.

BLAST FURNACE – A furnace in which mixed charges of oxide ores, fluxes, and fuels, are blown with a continuous blast of hot air and oxygen-enriched air for the chemical reduction of metals to their metallic state. Iron ore is most commonly treated in this way, and so are some ores of copper, lead, etc.

BLAST HOLE – A hole drilled for purposes of blasting rather than for exploration or geological information.

BLISTER COPPER – The product of the Bessemer converter furnace used in copper smelting. It is a crude form of copper, assaying about 99% copper, and requires further refining before being used for industrial purposes.

BLOCK CAVING – A cheap method of mining in which large blocks of ore are undercut, the ore breaking and caving under its own weight.

BONANZA – Very rich ore, or situation.

BOULDER CLAY – An unstratified deposit of clay in which are embedded rock particles up to the size of boulders; usually of glacial origin.

BOX HOLE – A short raise or opening driven above a drift for the purpose of drawing ore from a stope, or to permit access.

BREAST – A working face, usually restricted to a stope.

BRECCIA – A type of rock whose components are angular in shape, as distinguished from a conglomerate whose components are water-worn into a rounded shape.

BRUNTON COMPASS – A pocket compass equipped with sights and a reflector, useful for sighting lines, measuring dip and carrying out preliminary surveys.

BULK SAMPLE – A large sample, frequently involving many tons, selected in such a manner as to be representative of the material being sampled.

BULLION – Metal in bars, ingots or other uncoined form.

BULL QUARTZ – A prospector's term describing white, coarse-grained, barren quartz.

BYPRODUCT – A secondary or additional mineral or mineral product.

CAGE – The conveyance used to transport men and equipment in a shaft.

CATHODE – A rectangular plate of metal produced by electrolytic refining which is melted into commercial shapes such as wirebars, billets, ingots, etc.

CEMENT COPPER – Copper which has been salvaged from its solution in groundwater or mine drainage water by precipitating on scrap iron, a process commonly used in the western United States.

CHALCOPYRITE – A sulphide mineral of copper and iron, being a common ore of copper.

CHANGE HOUSE – A special building constructed at a mine where the miner changes to his working clothes; also known as a **dry house.**

CHANNEL SAMPLE – A sample composed of pieces of vein or mineral deposit that have been cut out of a small trench or channel, usually about four inches wide and an inch or so deep.

CHUTE – An opening, usually constructed of timber and equipped with a gate, through which ore is drawn from a stope into mine cars.

CINNABAR – A vermilion-colored ore of mercury.

CLAIM – A portion of mining land held under federal or provincial law. The common size is 1,320 ft. (approx. 400 m) square, containing 40 acres (about 16 hectares).

CLOSED CIRCUIT – A loop in a process wherein a selected portion of the product of a machine is returned to the head of the machine for finishing to required specification; commonly used examples in milling plants include grinding mills in closed circuit with classifiers.

COLLAR – The term applied to the timbering or concrete around the mouth of a shaft; also used to describe the top of a drill hole.

COMPLEX ORE – An ore containing a number of minerals of economic value, usually implying difficulty to extract the valuable metals.

COMPRESSOR – A machine for compressing air to a pressure sufficient to actuate mine machinery.

CONCENTRATE – A product containing the valuable metal and from which most of the waste material in the ore has been eliminated.

CONCENTRATOR – A milling plant that produces a concentrate of the valuable minerals or metals. Further treatment is required to recover the pure metal.

CONGLOMERATE – A sedimentary rock consisting of rounded, water-worn pebbles or boulders cemented into a solid mass.

CONTACT – The line or plane along which two different rocks come together.

CONVERTER – In copper smelting, a Bessemer furnace is used to separate copper metal from matte; also used in steelmaking.

CORE – The long cylinder of rock, about one inch or more in diameter, that is recovered by the diamond drill.

CORE BARREL – That part of a string of tools in diamond drilling in which the core specimen collects.

COUNTRY ROCK – A loose term to describe the general mass of rock adjacent to an orebody, as distinguished from the vein or ore deposit itself.

CROSSCUT – A horizontal opening driven across the course of a vein or structure, or in general across the strike of the rock formations; a connection from a shaft to an ore structure.

CRUSHER – A machine for crushing rock, such as a gyratory crusher, jaw crusher, stamp mill, etcetera.

CUT-AND-FILL – A method of stoping in which ore is removed in slices, or lifts, following which the excavation is filled with rock or other waste material known as backfill, before the subsequent slice is mined; the backfill supports the walls of the stope.

CUT VALUE – Applies to assays that have been reduced to some arbitrary maximum; thus high erratic values are reduced in order not to have an undue influence on the overall average.

CYANIDATION – A method of extracting gold or silver by dissolving it in a weak solution of sodium cyanide.

DEVELOPMENT – The underground work carried out for the purpose of opening up a mineral deposit. It includes shaft sinking, crosscutting, drifting and raising.

DIABASE – A common basic igneous rock usually occurring in dikes or sills.

DIAMOND – A very hard mineral, composed of pure carbon, which is set into a bit for drilling holes in rock.

DIAMOND DRILL – A rotary type of rock drill in which the cutting is done by abrasion rather than percussion. The cutting bit is set with diamonds and is attached to the end of long hollow rods through which water is pumped to the cutting face. The drill cuts a **core** of rock which is recovered in long cylindrical sections, an inch or more in diameter.

DIFFERENTIAL FLOTATION – A milling process by which each of the valuable minerals is floated and separated from the waste constituents of the ore.

DIKE – A long and relatively thin body of igneous rock that, while in the molten state, has intruded a fissure in older rocks and solidified.

DILUTION – Waste or low grade rock which is unavoidably removed along with the ore in the mining process.

DIP – The angle at which a vein, structure or rock bed is inclined from the horizontal, measured at right angles to the strike.

DIP NEEDLE – A compass whose needle is mounted so as to swing in a vertical plane, used for determining the magnetic attraction of rocks.

DISSEMINATED ORE – Ore carrying small particles of valuable minerals, spread more or less uniformly through the gangue matter; distinct from **massive** ore wherein the valuable minerals occur in almost solid form with very little waste material included.

DRAG FOLD — Where rock has been folded or bent back on itself.

DRIFT (DRIVE) — A horizontal passage underground that follows along the length of a vein or rock formation as opposed to a crosscut which crosses the rock formation.

DRIFTER — A rock drill used for boring horizontal holes for blasting.

DRY HOUSE — A building where the miner changes to his working clothes.

DUMP — A pile or heap of rock or ore on surface.

ELECTROLYTIC REFINING — The process of refining metals by casting into **anodes** which are placed in an **electrolyte** consisting usually of a salt of the same metal dissolved in water, and depositing on a **cathode** by pressing an electric current into the system; similarly, by using an electrically inert anode, and depositing the metal on the cathode from a purified solution of a salt of the metal.

EM SURVEY — A geophysical survey which measures the electromagnetic property of the rocks.

EN ECHELON — A term used to describe a formation in which the occurrences are found in roughly parallel but staggered fashion.

ERA — A large division of geologic time. E.g., Precambrian era.

EROSION — The breaking down and subsequent removal of either rock or earthy surface material through the forces of nature.

EXPLORATION — The prospecting, diamond drilling and other work involved in searching for ore.

FACE — The end of a drift, crosscut or stope in which work is progressing.

FAULT — A break in the earth's crust caused by forces which have moved the rock on one side with respect to the other; faults may extend for miles, or be only a few inches in length; similarly, the movement or displacement along the fault may vary widely.

FERROUS — Containing iron.

FINE GOLD — Fineness is the proportion of pure gold or silver in jewelry or bullion expressed in parts per thousand. Thus, 925 fine gold indicates 925 parts out of 1,000, or 92.5%, is pure gold. A fine ounce is a troy ounce of 99.5% gold and 0.5% silver.

FISSURE — An extensive crack, break or fracture in rocks.

FLOAT — Pieces of rock that have been broken off and moved from their original location by natural forces such as frost action or glaciers.

FLOTATION — A milling process by which some mineral particles are induced to become attached to bubbles and float, and others to sink. In this way the valuable minerals are concentrated and separated from the worthless gangue.

FLOWSHEET — The sequence of operations, step by step, by which ore is treated in a milling, concentration, or smelting process.

FLUX — A chemical substance used in metallurgy to react with gangue minerals to form **slags** which are liquid at the furnace temperatures concerned, and low enough in density to float on the molten bath of metal or matte; examples range in scale from large tonnages of limestone, silica, etc., in large furnaces, to small quantities of borax, soda, etc., used in laboratory assay fusions.

FOLD — Any bending or wrinkling of a rock strata.

FOOTWALL — The wall or rock on the underside of a vein or ore structure.

FRACTURE — As the name implies, is a break in the rock. The opening affords the opportunity for entry of mineral bearing solutions. A cross-fracture is a minor break extending at more or less right angles to the direction of the principal fractures.

FREE MILLING — Ores of gold or silver from which the precious metals can be recovered by concentrating methods without resort to roasting or chemical treatment.

FRICTION HOIST — A mine hoist in which conveyances are suspended from both sides of a simple friction pulley which imparts the desired motion; it is distinct from a drum hoist in which the ropes are wound onto their individual drums.

GABBRO — A coarse grained dark igneous rock.

GALENA — A sulphide mineral of lead, being a common lead ore.

GAMMA — A unit of measurement of magnetic intensity.

GANGUE — The worthless minerals in an ore deposit.

GEIGER COUNTER — An instrument used to measure radioactivity (e.g., that which emanates from certain minerals) by means of a Geiger-Mueller tube. It detects the gamma rays and indicates the frequency or intensity either visually (by dial or flashing light), audibly (by earphones) or both.

GEOLOGY — The science concerned with the study of the rocks which compose the earth.

GEOPHYSICAL SURVEY — A scientific method of prospecting that measures the physical properties of rock formations. Common properties investigated include magnetism, specific gravity, electrical conductivity and radioactivity.

GLACIAL DRIFT — Sedimentary material consisting of clay and boulders which has been transported by glaciers.

GLACIAL STRIAE — Lines or scratches on a smooth rock surface caused by glacial abrasion.

GLORY HOLE — An open pit from which ore is extracted, especially where broken ore is passed to underground workings before being hoisted.

GNEISS — a layered or banded crystalline metamorphic rock whose grains are aligned or elongated into a roughly parallel arrangement.

GOSSAN — The rust colored oxidized capping or staining of a mineral deposit, generally formed by the oxidation or alteration of iron sulphides.

GOUGE — Fine, putty-like material composed of ground-up rock found along a fault.

GRAB SAMPLE — A sample taken at random; it is assayed to determine if valuable elements are contained in the rock. A grab sample is not intended to be representative of the deposit, and usually the best looking material is selected.

GRAVITY METER, GRAVIMETER — An instrument for measuring the gravitational attraction of the earth which varies with the density of the rocks in the vicinity.

GREENSTONE — A convenient field term used to describe any fine-grained greenish volcanic rock, most often applied to andesite.

GRIZZLY — A grating (usually constructed of steel rails) placed over the top of a chute or ore pass for the purpose of stopping the larger pieces of rock or ore.

GROSS VALUE — The theoretical value of ore determined simply by applying the assay of metal or metals, and the current market price; it represents the total value of the contained metals before deduction for recovery losses, mining and smelting costs, etc.; it must be used only with caution and severe qualification.

GROUTING — The process of sealing off a water flow in rocks by forcing thin cement slurry, or other chemicals into the crevices; usually done through a diamond drill hole.

GRUBSTAKE — Finances or supplies of food, etcetera, furnished a prospector in return for an interest in any discoveries made.

GUIDES — The timber rails along the sides of a shaft for the purpose of steadying, or guiding, the cage or conveyance.

HANGING WALL — The wall or rock on the upper side of a vein or ore deposit.

HEMATITE — An iron oxide mineral, one of the commonest ores of iron.

HIGH GRADE — Rich ore. As a verb, it refers to selective mining of the best ore in a deposit.

HIGHGRADER — One who steals rich ore, especially gold, from a mine.

HOIST — The machine used for raising and lowering the cage or other conveyance in a shaft.

HORSE — A mass of waste rock lying within a vein or orebody.

HOST ROCK — The rock surrounding an ore deposit.

HYDROMETALLURGY — The treatment of ores by wet processes (e.g., leaching) resulting in the solution of some component and its subsequent recovery.

IGNEOUS ROCKS — Rocks formed by the solidification of molten material that originated within the earth.

ILMENITE – An ore of titanium, being an iron-titanium oxide.

INDUCED POLARIZATION – A method of ground geophysical surveying employing an electrical current to determine indications of mineralization.

INDUSTRIAL MINERALS – Usually non-metallic minerals which are used in industry and manufacturing processes in their natural state, though with some beneficiation to imposed specifications; examples include asbestos, salt, gravels, building materials, talc, sands, etcetera.

INTRUSIVE – A body of igneous rock formed by the consolidation of magma intruded into other rocks, in contrast to lavas, which are extruded upon the surface.

ION EXCHANGE – An exchange of ions in a crystal with ions in a solution. Used as a method for recovering valuable metals in solution. E.g., uranium.

JAW CRUSHER – A machine in which the rock is broken by the action of moving steel jaws.

JIG – An apparatus used in milling to concentrate ore on a screen submerged in water, either by a reciprocating motion of the screen or by the pulsation of water through it.

KEEWATIN – Consisting mostly of lavas, but including some sediments, the Keewatin series is perhaps the oldest of the Precambrian rocks.

KOEPE HOIST – *See* **friction hoist.**

LAGGING – Planks or small timbers placed along the roof of a stope or drift to prevent rocks from falling, rather than to support the main weight of the overlying rocks.

LAMPROPHYRE – A rock composed of dark minerals which occurs in the form of dikes.

LATERITE – A residual soil developed in tropical countries from which the silica has been leached. May be an ore of iron, nickel, manganese.

LAUNDER – A chute or trough for conveying pulp, water or powdered ore in the milling process.

LAVA – A general name for the molten rock ejected by volcanoes.

LEACHING – A chemical process for the extraction of valuable minerals from ore; also, the natural process by which ground waters dissolve minerals, thus leaving the rock with a smaller proportion of some of the minerals than it contained originally.

LENS – Generally used to describe a body of ore that is thick in the middle and tapers towards the ends.

LENTICULAR – A lens-shaped deposit having roughly the form of a double convex lens.

LEVEL – The horizontal passages on a working horizon in a mine; it is customary to work mines from a shaft, establishing levels at regular intervals, generally about 50 meters or more apart.

LIMESTONE – A bedded sedimentary deposit consisting chiefly of calcium carbonate.

LIMONITE – A brown hydrous iron oxide.

LINE CUTTING – Lines cleared through the bush to permit sights to be taken for geophysical and other surveys.

LINE DRIVE – A horizontal opening which follows a straight course, usually along the strike of the rock formations.

LODE – A mineral deposit in solid rock.

LONG TON – Contains 2,240 lbs. avoirdupois.

LONGWALL – A method of stoping which extracts all of the zone being mined, used particularly in coal mining.

MAGMA – The molten material deep in the earth from which rocks are formed.

MAGNETIC SEPARATION – A process in which a magnetically susceptible mineral is separated from gangue minerals by applying a strong magnetic field; ores of iron are commonly treated in this way.

MAGNETITE – Magnetic iron ore, being a black iron oxide containing 72.4% iron when pure.

MAGNETOMETER – An instrument used to measure the magnetic attraction of underlying rocks.

MARGINAL ORE DEPOSIT – An orebody of minimal profitability.

MATRIX – The rock or gangue material containing ore minerals.

MATTE – The product of a smelter, being metal with some contained sulphur. It must be further refined to obtain the pure metal.

METALLURGY – The process of extracting metals from their ores.

METAMORPHIC ROCKS – Rocks that have undergone a change in texture or composition from their original form through such agencies as heat, pressure.

METAMORPHISM – The process of changing the form or structure of rocks through various natural agencies such as heat and pressure.

MILL – (a) a plant in which ore is treated for the recovery of valuable metals, or concentration of the valuable minerals into a smaller bulk for shipment to a smelter or other reduction works; (b) a machine consisting of a revolving drum, for the fine grinding of ores as a preparation for treatment.

MILL HEADS – The average grade of ore fed into a mill.

MILLING ORE – Ore that contains sufficient valuable mineral to be treated by milling process.

MINERAL – A naturally occurring homogeneous substance having definite physical properties and chemical composition and, if formed under favorable conditions, a definite crystal form.

MUCK – Ore or rock that has been broken by blasting.

MUSKEG – Decayed vegetable matter and black soil forming swampy areas.

NATIVE METAL — A metal which has occurred in nature pure or uncombined with other substances.

NUGGET — A water-worn piece of precious metal, usually implying some size.

OPEN CUT — A surface working, open to daylight, such as a quarry. Also referred to as open pit or open cast mine.

ORE — A mixture of ore minerals and gangue from which at least one of the metals can be extracted at a profit.

ORE DRESSING — The treatment of ore by the removal of some of the waste materials.

ORE RESERVES — The prime measured assets of a mine as to tonnage and grade. They may be classified as **positive** or **proven, probable,** or **possible,** in decreasing degree of statistical confidence as to the accuracy of their expressed tonnage and grade; other terms frequently applied include: **measured, indicated, geological, broken reserves,** etcetera.

ORESHOOT — The portion, or length, of the vein, or other ore structure, that carries sufficient valuable mineral to be profitable to mine.

OUTCROP — An exposure of rock or a mineral deposit that can be seen on surface, i.e., it is not covered by overburden or water.

OXIDATION — A chemical reaction caused by natural forces that results in a change in the composition of a mineral.

PAN — To wash in a pan, gravel and sand, or rock samples that have been ground to small particles, in order to separate gold or other valuable metals.

PARTY LINE — Refers to the boundary between two properties. Under most mining laws, an underground heading cannot be carried within a prescribed distance of a boundary without permission of the owners of the adjoining ground.

PEGMATITE — A coarse grained igneous rock usually irregular in texture and composition, similar to a granite in composition; it usually occurs in dikes or veins and sometimes contains valuable minerals.

PELLET — A marble-sized ball of iron mineral bonded by clay material, and fused for hardness.

PICKET LINE — A reference line, marked by pickets or stakes, established on a property for mapping and survey purposes.

PIG IRON — Crude cast iron from a blast furnace.

PILLAR — A block of solid ore or rock left in place for the purpose of supporting the shaft, walls or roof in a mine.

PITCH — *See* **plunge.**

PITCHBLENDE — An important uranium ore mineral, containing a high percentage of uranium oxide. It is black in color, possesses a characteristic pitch-like or greasy lustre, and is highly radioactive.

PLACER — An alluvial deposit of sand and gravel containing

valuable minerals such as gold, tin, etc.

PLANT — A group of buildings, and their contained equipment, in which a process or function is carried out; on a mine it will include warehouses, hoisting equipment, compressors, repair shops, offices, mill or concentrator.

PLUNGE — The vertical angle an orebody makes between the horizontal plane and the direction along which it extends, longitudinally to depth.

PLUTONIC — Referring to rocks of igneous origin that have come from great depth.

PORPHYRY — Any igneous rock in which relatively large, conspicuous crystals (called phenocrysts) are set in a fine-grained groundmass.

PORPHYRY COPPER — A deposit of disseminated copper minerals in a large body of porphyry.

PORTAL — The surface entrance to a tunnel or adit.

POSITIVE ORE — *See* **ore reserves.**

POSSIBLE ORE — *See* **ore reserves.**

PROBABLE ORE — *See* **ore reserves.**

PROSPECT — A mining property, the value of which has not been proved by exploration.

PROVEN ORE — *See* **ore reserves.**

PULP — Pulverized or ground ore in solution.

PYRITE — A common sulphide mineral, shiny and yellow in color, composed of sulphur and iron, sometimes known as "fool's gold."

PYRRHOTITE — An iron sulphide, less common than pyrite, bronze in color and magnetic; sometimes is associated with nickel, in which case it may be mined as a nickel ore.

RADIOACTIVITY — The property of spontaneously emitting alpha, beta or gamma rays by the disintegration of the nuclei of atoms.

RAISE — A vertical or inclined underground working that has been excavated from the bottom upward.

RAKE — Similar to **plunge** (*See*), being the trend of an orebody along the direction of its strike.

REAMING SHELL — A component of a string of rods used in diamond drilling; it is set with diamonds, and placed between the bit and the core barrel to maintain the gauge of the hole.

RECONNAISSANCE — A preliminary survey of ground.

RECOVERY — The percentage of valuable metal in the ore that is recovered by metallurgical treatment.

REFRACTORY ORE — One that resists the action of chemical reagents in the normal treatment processes, and which may require roasting or other means to effect the full recovery of the valuable minerals.

REPLACEMENT ORE — Ore formed by a process during which certain minerals have passed into solution and have been carried away, while valuable minerals from the solution have been deposited in the place of those removed.

RESERVES — *See* **ore reserves.**

RESISTIVITY SURVEY — A geophysical technique which measures the resistance to an electric current presented by the various rock formations through which it passes.

RESUING — A method of stoping wherein the wall rock on one side of the vein has been blasted before the ore itself is broken; it is employed on narrow veins (say less than 30 inches) and permits recovery of the ore with minimum dilution.

REVERBERATORY FURNACE — A long, flat furnace used in smelting copper concentrates; its principal function is the slagging of gangue minerals, and the production of **matte.**

ROASTING — The treatment of ore by heat and air, or oxygen-enriched air, in order to burn off sulphur and arsenic.

ROCK — Any naturally formed combination of minerals forming an appreciable part of the earth's crust.

ROCKBOLTING — The act of consolidating roof strata by means of anchoring and tensioning steel bolts in holes especially drilled for the purpose.

ROCK BURST — The sudden failure of walls or pillars in a mine caused by the weight or pressure of the surrounding rocks, and accompanied by a violent release of energy.

ROCK FACTOR — An inverse expression of the density of a rock or an ore, expressed as the number of cubic feet per ton. E.g., highly siliceous ores may occupy 13 cu. ft. per ton in the solid state while heavy sulphide ores may be contained in as little as 8 cu. ft. per ton.

ROCK MECHANICS — A study of stress conditions surrounding mine openings, and the ability of rocks and underground structures to withstand imposed stresses.

ROD MILL — A rotating cylindrical mill which employs steel rods as a grinding medium.

ROOM AND PILLAR — A method of mining flat-lying deposits in which the mined area, or rooms, are separated by pillars of approximately equal size.

ROTARY DRILL — A drilling machine that rotates a rigid, tubular string of rods to which is attached a bit for cutting rock to produce bore holes. Commonly employed to drill holes for blasting in open pit mining operations; also, for drilling oil wells.

ROYALTY — The amount paid by the lessee or operator to the owner of the mineral land, generally based on a certain amount per ton or a percentage of the total production or profits. Also, the fee paid for the right to use a patented process.

RUN-OF-MINE — A loose term sometimes used to describe ore of average grade.

SALTING — Introducing particles of metal or mineral into a deposit or samples, resulting in assays that are higher than the actual metal content; done either accidentally or with intent to defraud.

SAMPLE — A small portion of rock or mineral deposit, usually taken for the purpose of being assayed to determine the content of valuable elements.

SAMPLING — Selecting a fractional but representative part of a deposit for analysis.

SANDSTONE — A sedimentary rock composed of fine grains of quartz, etcetera, which have been cemented together.

SCALING — The act of removing loose slabs of rock from roofs and walls.

SCARP — An escarpment, cliff or steep slope along the margin of a plateau, mesa or terrace.

SCHIST — A foliated metamorphic rock whose grains have a roughly parallel arrangement; it is generally developed by shearing.

SCINTILLATION COUNTER — An instrument used for detecting and measuring radioactivity by detecting the gamma rays — more sensitive than the geiger counter.

SECONDARY ENRICHMENT — Enrichment of a vein or deposit by minerals which have been taken into solution from one part of the vein or adjacent rocks and redeposited in another.

SEDIMENTARY ROCKS — Secondary rocks formed from material which is derived from other rocks and which is laid down under water, e.g., limestone, shale, sandstone. A characteristic feature of sedimentary deposits is a layered structure known as bedding or stratification.

SEISMIC PROSPECTING — A geophysical method of prospecting utilizing the knowledge of the speed and reflection of sound waves in rock.

SELECTIVE FLOTATION — *See* **differential flotation.**

SELF POTENTIAL — In geophysical prospecting, a technique which recognizes and measures the minute electric currents generated by sulphide deposits.

SHAFT — A vertical or inclined excavation for the purpose of opening and servicing a mine. It is usually equipped with a hoist at the top, which lowers and raises a conveyance for handling men and material.

SHALE — Sedimentary rock formed by the consolidation of mud or silt.

SHEAR OR SHEARING — The deformation of rocks by lateral movement along innumerable parallel planes, generally resulting from pressure, and producing such metamorphic structures as cleavage and schistosity.

SHEAR ZONE — A zone in which shearing has occurred on a large scale.

SHEAVE WHEEL – A large grooved wheel placed in the top of a headframe, over which the hoisting rope passes.

SHOOT – A concentration of mineral values; that part of a vein or zone carrying values of ore grade.

SHORT TON – Contains 2,000 lb. avoirdupois.

SHRINKAGE STOPE – A method of stoping which utilizes part of the broken ore as a working platform and as support for the walls.

SIDERITE – Iron carbonate, being an iron ore that contains 48.2% iron when pure. Before it can be utilized in the blast furnace, it must be roasted to drive off the contained carbon dioxide, the resulting product being called **sinter.**

SILICA – An oxide of silicon, of which quartz is a common example.

SILICEOUS – Containing an abundance of quartz.

SILL – An intrusive sheet of igneous rock of approximately uniform thickness and generally extending over a considerable lateral extent; it has been forced between level, or gently-inclined, beds.

SILT – A general name for the muddy deposits of fine sediment usually found on the bottom of lakes.

SINTER – The heat treatment of fine ore particles to produce larger pieces for blast furnace feed.

SKIP – A self-dumping type of bucket used in a shaft for hoisting ore or rock.

SLAG – The vitreous mass separated from the fused metals in a smelting process.

SLASH – Rock blasted from the side of a drift, resulting in the widening of the opening; it may be done to ascertain the width of the ore, or merely to make more working room.

SLICKENSIDE – The striated polished surface of a fault caused by one wall rubbing against the other.

SPELTER – The zinc of commerce, more or less impure, cast from molten metal into slabs or ingots.

SPHALERITE – a sulphide mineral of zinc, being a common zinc ore.

SQUARE SET – A set of timbers used for support in underground mining, consisting of cap, girt and post.

STATION – An enlargement of a shaft made at the level horizon used primarily for the storage and handling of equipment.

STOCK PILE – Broken ore accumulated in a heap on surface, pending treatment or shipment.

STOPE – An excavation in a mine from which ore is being or has been extracted.

STRIKE – The direction, that is the course or bearing, of a vein or rock formation measured on a horizontal surface.

STRINGER – A narrow vein or irregular filament of mineral traversing a rock mass.

STRIP — To remove the overburden or barren rock overlying an orebody.

STRIP MINE, MINING — The removal of earth, rock and other material to expose a coal seam or other near-surface deposit, generally mined by power shovels.

SUBLEVEL — An intermediate level or working horizon in a mine opened between main working levels.

SULPHIDE — A compound of sulphur with another element.

SUMP — An excavation for the purpose of catching or storing water in an underground working or at the bottom of a shaft.

SYNCLINE — A downarched fold in bedded or stratified rocks.

TACONITE — A term common on the Mesabi iron range for a siliceous iron formation, containing magnetite and hematite, that has to be concentrated to produce a useable iron ore.

TAILINGS — Material rejected from a mill after the recoverable valuable minerals have been extracted.

TALUS — A heap of broken coarse rock found at the foot of a cliff or mountain.

TELLURIDE — A compound of tellurium with another element, often gold or silver.

THICKENER — A large round tank in a mill for the separation of solids from a solution, the clear liquid overflowing the tank whereas the rock particles sink to the bottom.

TONS-PER-VERTICAL-FOOT — A common expression to describe the measure of an ore deposit. It is arrived at by multiplying the ore length by its width and dividing by the appropriate **rock factor;** it is the amount of ore for each foot of depth; thus an orebody that shows 1,000 tons per vertical foot would, if it carried down for 100 ft., contain 100,000 tons.

TRAM — To haul cars of ore or waste in a mine.

TRENCH — A long, narrow excavation dug through overburden, or blasted out of rock, to expose a vein or ore structure.

TUBE MILL — An apparatus consisting of a revolving cylinder about half filled with steel rods or balls and into which crushed ore is fed for fine grinding.

TUFF — A rock composed of fine material such as ash that has been explosively ejected from a volcano.

TUNNEL — A horizontal underground passage that is open to the atmosphere at both ends.

UMPIRE SAMPLE or ASSAY — An assay made by a third party to provide a basis for settlement of value between the buyer and seller of ore.

UNCUT VALUE — The actual assay value as opposed to the cut value which has been reduced by some arbitrary formula.

URANINITE — A uranium mineral carrying a high percentage of uranium oxide, frequently found in pegmatite dikes.

VEIN – A fissure, fault or crack in a rock filled by minerals that have travelled upwards from some deep source.

VOLCANIC ROCKS – The class of igneous rocks that have been poured out or ejected at or near the earth's surface, as from a volcano.

VUG – A small cavity occurring in vein or ore deposit. It is frequently lined with well formed crystals, such as amethyst.

WAGON DRILL – A reciprocating type of drill mounted on a truck or light, wheeled carriage, and which usually employs long drill steel to drill vertical or inclined holes for blasting.

WALL ROCK – The rock forming the walls of a vein or ore deposit. Sometimes referred to as country rock.

WASTE – Barren rock in a mine, or at least material that is too low in grade to be of economic value.

WEATHERING – The chemical and mechanical breakdown of rocks and minerals under the action of atmospheric agencies. Eventually, surface rocks crumble into soil.

WEDGE – As used in diamond drilling, refers to the placing of a wedge at some point in the hole for the purpose of deflecting the bit in another direction.

WINZE – A vertical or inclined opening sunk from a point inside a mine. Similar to a shaft, but the latter starts at surface.

WIREBAR COPPER – Refined copper that has been cast into a shape convenient for feeding to wire-drawing machines.

ZONE – Is an area or region which is distinct from the surrounding rock either because of a difference in the type or structure of rocks, or because of mineralization.

ZONE OF OXIDATION – The upper part of a mineral deposit that has become oxidized.

Oil Terms

ACIDIZING – A technique for increasing the permeability *(See)* of acid-soluble rocks by pumping hydrochloric or hydrofluoric acid into the formation. Can be combined with fracturing *(See)*.

ALLOWABLE PRODUCTION – The maximum rate of production per well or field permitted by regulatory authorities in order to ensure maximum use of reservoir energy *(See)*, or to prorate production to market demand.

ANNULUS – The ring-like space between casing and borehole, or between two sets of casing or tubing.

ANTICLINE – A stratified rock mass folded so that it is convex upward. A **syncline** is convex downward.

BARREL OF OIL – 35 Imperial or 42 U.S. gallons.

BLOW-OUT – An uncontrolled expulsion of formation fluid through the wellhead.

BLOW-OUT PREVENTER (B.O.P.) – A hydraulically operated wellhead attachment designed to prevent blow-outs by closing the borehole in case of emergency.

CASING – A string of protective pipe lowered into a borehole to prevent the walls from caving in and to facilitate drilling and production operations.

CHRISTMAS TREE – An assembly of valves and gauges for the control of oil or gas flowing thrugh the wellhead.

COMPLETION – The preparation of a well for production.

CORE – A cylindrical rock sample obtained by drilling with a ring-shaped bit at the end of a **core barrel.**

CRUDE OIL – A liquid mixture of hydrocarbons *(See)* and minor impurities produced from an oil reservoir.

DEADWEIGHT TONNAGE (dwt) – The carrying capacity of a tanker in long tons. 1 long ton = 2,240 pounds = 1.016 metric tons.

DEPLETION ALLOWANCE – Authorized deduction from production income for tax purposes, granted for the depletion of non-renewable reserves.

DEVELOPMENT DRILLING – Drilling for the purpose of exploiting a known oil or gas accumulation.

DOLOMITE – A sedimentary rock consisting primarily of the mineral dolomite, a calcium-magnesium carbonate, $CaMg(CO_3)_2$.

DOLOMITIZATION – The partial replacement in a limestone formation of calcite by dolomite. Since the mineral dolomite takes less room than calcite, dolomitization generally means increased porosity.

DRAINAGE UNIT – The maximum area of an oil or gas pool that can be drained efficiently by one well.

DRILLER – The foreman of a drilling crew. Each drilling rig is manned by three crews working round-the-clock in 8-hour shifts (see Tour).

DRILLSHIP – A converted or specially built ship with a drilling rig mounted on deck. The drill pipe runs through a hole, the **moon-pool,** in the bottom of the vessel.

DRY AND ABANDONED (D&A) – The fate of an unsuccessful well. "Dry" refers to the absence of oil or gas in commercial quantities, not to the absence of formation fluids.

ENHANCED RECOVERY – Any secondary or tertiary recovery method *(See).*

EXPLORATION DRILLING – Drilling for a suspected, but yet undiscovered oil or gas pool. Also called **wildcatting.**

FACIES – A term applied to the sum of characteristics that distinguish one rock type from another. A formation can have a sandstone facies and a shale facies, a near-shore facies and an offshore facies.

FARMOUT – The assignment of oil and gas rights to another operator.

FEEDSTOCKS – Petroleum products as raw materials for petrochemical plants.

FISH – Any foreign object lost in the borehole that must be fished out before drilling can continue.

FRACTURING – A technique of pumping fluid into a formation under sufficiently high pressure to widen existing, or create new cracks, which are then propped open by coarse sand, glass beads or other grains contained in the injected fluid. Fracturing can be combined with acidizing *(See)*. Also called **fraccing** (sometimes spelt "fracing").

FREEHOLD LAND – Land in which the owner and not the state holds the mineral rights.

GAS CAP – Gas occupying the upper part of an oil and gas trap.

GAS CAP DRIVE – Reservoir energy *(See)* for an oil pool provided by the expansion of overlying gas.

HYDROCARBONS – Organic chemical compounds of hydrogen (H) and carbon (C). The simplest is methane, CH_4. *(See* also Petroleum.)*

IN SITU – Latin for "in its original place". In petroleum engineering the term is applied to various methods of mobilizing heavy and tar sands oils in the subsurface reservoir ("in situ") before they can be produced through conventional wells.

ISOPACH MAP – A map showing the thickness variations of a rock unit.

JACK-UP PLATFORM – An offshore drilling platform that can lower its legs to the sea floor and jack itself up into a working position above sea level.

KNOCKING – Premature ignition of gasoline in an internal combustion engine. See also Octane Rating.

LANDMAN – An employee or consultant (male or female) specializing in the acquisition and administration of oil, gas, and surface rights.

LIMESTONE – A sedimentary rock consisting primarily of the mineral calcite (calcium carbonate, $CaCO_3$).

LIQUEFIED PETROLEUM GAS (LPG) – Butane and propane shipped and sold in liquid form.

LITHOLOGY – The physical character, especially the mineral composition of a rock.

MOON-POOL – The hole in the bottom of a drillship through which the drill pipe runs.

MUD – A specially prepared drilling fluid that lubricates and cools the drill bit, neutralizes the formation pressure, and helps to prevent the walls of the borehole from caving in.

OCTANE RATING – A measure of the resistance of a motor gasoline to **knocking** *(See)*. Expressed in points on an arbitrary scale on which octane (a hydrocarbon compound) is assigned 100 points.

OIL AND GAS RIGHTS — The right to explore for, and produce oil and gas under a certain parcel of land.

OIL IN PLACE — All oil contained in a natural reservoir, as opposed to the recoverable portion.

OIL SAND — Any sandstone containing crude oil.

PACKER — An expandable rubber attachment to the drillstem used to isolate one part of the borehole or casing from another.

PAYOUT — The recovery of the drilling and completion costs of a well from the proceeds of production.

PERFORATING — The shooting of holes through casing and cement with a downhole gun.

PERMEABILITY — A measure of the capacity of a formation to transmit fluid. Depends on the size, shape and continuity of connected pore space. *(See* also Porosity.)

PETROLEUM — A liquid mixture of naturally occurring hydrocarbons *(See)*. In the wider sense petroleum includes natural gas.

PETROLEUM PROVINCE — A large oil- or gas-producing region; often, but not necessarily identical with a sedimentary basin *(See)*.

POROSITY — The volume of pore space in a rock unit. Expressed as a percentage of the total rock volume. *(See* also Permeability.)

PRIMARY RECOVERY — Petroleum production under natural reservoir energy *(See)* and by simple pumping, without the use of enhanced recovery methods.

PRODUCER — A producing oil or gas well. Also the owner of such a well.

PROVEN RESERVES — The portion of an oil or gas reserve that has been established by development drilling and that is economically producible with present technology.

RECOVERABLE OIL — Oil that can be produced from a natural reservoir by primary, secondary, or tertiary recovery methods *(See)*.

REEF — A ridge or mound built by corals or other marine organisms.

REFINERY — A plant for the conversion of crude oil into petroleum products.

REFLECTION SEISMOGRAPH — An instrument for the recording of elastic (shock) waves reflected by a subsurface rock formation.

REFLECTOR — A rock surface capable of reflecting seismic waves.

RESERVOIR ENERGY — The subsurface pressure under which formation fluid is driven into the borehole.

RIGHT-OF-WAY — The right of passage or usage. The term also refers to the strip of land to which the right applies.

ROYALTY — The share of production due to the holder of

the oil and gas rights under the well location.

SECONDARY RECOVERY – Petroleum production under reservoir energy *(See)* artificially enhanced by the injection of fluid or gas.

SEDIMENTARY BASIN – A large depression in the earth's crust in which sediments accumulated during long geological periods. Examples are the Western Canada Sedimentary Basin and the Sverdrup Basin in the Canadian Arctic.

SEISMOGRAM – A graphic record of shock waves registered by a seismograph.

SEMI-SUBMERSIBLE – An offshore drilling platform whose floats are at sea level in the transport, and semi-submersed in the drilling mode.

SHOTPOINT – A point in a seismic survey at which a shock wave is generated, usually by "shooting", i.e. by setting off an explosion in a **shothole** drilled for this purpose.

SHUT-IN WELL – A well capable of producing, but temporarily closed for technical or economic reasons.

SOLUTION-GAS DRIVE – Reservoir energy *(See)* for an oil pool provided by the expansion of gas dissolved in the oil.

SOUR GAS – Natural gas contaminated with sulphur compounds.

SPUDDING – The start of a drilling operation by sinking a large-diameter surface hole.

STRATIGRAPHIC TRAP – A petroleum reservoir formed primarily by sedimentary (rather than structural) processes.

STRATIGRAPHY – A branch of geology that deals with the history and properties of sedimentary rocks in their normal sequence.

STRUCTURE – A rock mass shaped by folding or faulting.

STRUCTURAL TRAP – A petroleum reservoir formed by folding or faulting, such as anticlines and fault traps.

STIMULATION – Any measure, such as acidizing or fracturing *(See)* designed to increase the natural permeability of a producing formation.

SWEET GAS – Natural gas not contaminated with sulphur compounds.

TAR SAND – An oil-saturated sand from which the lighter hydrocarbons have escaped, leaving the viscous bitumen behind.

TERTIARY RECOVERY – Petroleum production methods designed to improve the efficiency of secondary recovery methods *(See)* by increasing the mobility of the oil in place with heat or chemicals.

TESTING OR DRILLSTEM TESTING – A method of placing a well on temporary production in order to establish the presence of oil or gas, either at the bottom of the open borehole or behind the perforated casing.

TIGHT HOLE – A well, the results of which are kept secret in order to protect the operator's competitive advantage.

TOOL PUSH OR TOOL PUSHER – The supervisor of a drilling operation.

TOTAL DEPTH (T.D.) – The final depth reached by a well.

TOWNSHIP – The basic land survey unit in western North America. A standard township measures 6 by 6 miles and is divided into 36 sections of 1 square mile each.

TRAP – A porous rock mass capable of collecting oil or gas under a roof of impermeable rocks.

TUBING – A removable string of pipe installed in a well for the production of oil or gas.

UNCONFORMITY – A gap in the geologic record represented by the contact between an older and a substantially younger set of formations. If the two sets are not parallel, the unconformity is **angular.**

UNITIZATION – The **pooling** of a number of producing leases, especially for the purpose of enhanced recovery *(See)*.

WATER DRIVE – Reservoir energy *(See)* for oil or gas production, provided by the pressure of an underlying water column.

WATER FLOOD – A common secondary recovery method in which water injected into the formation drives part of the remaining oil toward the producing wells.

WELLHEAD – The top of the cased borehole.

WELL LOGGING – The electric recording by downhole instruments of the physical properties of the penetrated formations and their fluid content.

WHIPSTOCK – A wedge-shaped steel tool inserted into the borehole to guide the drill in a predetermined direction.

WILDCAT – An exploratory well, especially one drilled far from previous well locations.

Financial Terms

AMORTIZATION – The funding of a capital cost which is then deemed to be retired in equalized payments of principal and interest over a given life of the capital asset.

AUTHORIZED CAPITAL – *See* Capital Stock.

BALANCE SHEET – Normally presented to shareholders once a year, it gives the financial condition of the company on some particular day, usually December 31st. The principle of a balance sheet is that for everything owned (assets) there must be an exactly equal amount of debts (liabilities) plus the value of the company's shares and retained earnings (net worth). The formula is: assets = liabilities + net worth.

BEAR MARKET — When share prices are going down.

BOARD LOT — A block of shares of some rounded number that can be conveniently traded. For example, for mining shares in Canada selling under $1.00 a board lot is 500 shares; under 10¢, 1,000 shares.

BONDS — These are debts against a corporation, government or municipality which are to be repaid on or before a specified date. Interest on the loan is paid at fixed rates and intervals.
Mortgage bonds backed by a pledge of specific property such as land, plant or equipment.
Collateral bonds are backed by a pledge of securities such as stocks or other bonds.
Debentures are backed only by the credit of the issuer and are used by governments and municipalities.

BROKERAGE — The commission fee, which is set by the stock exchange, charged by a broker on each purchase or sale. The rates are scaled according to the share price.

BULL MARKET — When prices are rising.

CALL — An option to buy shares at a specified price. The opposite of **put** *(See)*.

CAPITAL STOCK — The total ownership of a limited liability company divided among a specified number of shares.

CASH FLOW — A measurement of fiscal strength of a business by taking the net of the inflow and outflow of cash during an accounting period. It does not take account of depreciation or bookkeeping write-offs which do not involve an actual cash outlay.

CHARTER — A document issued by a governing authority creating a company or other corporation.

COMMON STOCK — These shares have full voting rights which the holders use to control the company in common with each other. There is no fixed or assured dividend as with preferred shares, which have first claim on the distribution of a company's earnings or assets.

CONFIRMATION — A form delivered by the broker to the client setting forth the details of stock sales or purchases for the client.

CUM-DIVIDEND — Buyer entitled to pending dividend payment.

CURRENT ASSETS — Are those which, in the ordinary course of business, can and are likely to be converted into cash within a year. Current assets include cash, marketable securities, accounts receivable and supplies.

CURRENT LIABILITIES — Are the debts of a company which are payable within a year's time.

DAY ORDER — Good only on day of entry.

DEBENTURES — *See* **bonds.**

DEFERRED CHARGES — Expenses which are incurred but which are not charged against the current year's operations.

DEPLETION — An accounting device, used primarily in tax computations which recognizes the consumption of the ore deposit which is a mine's principal asset.

DEPRECIATION — In accounting, the practice of deducting annually a specified amount or percentage from the value of equipment and machinery representative of the deterioration suffered by the equipment or machinery during the year. The deduction reduces the amount of profit reported but is not an actual out-of-pocket expense.

DISCOUNT — The minimum price below the par value at which treasury shares may legally be sold.

DIVIDEND CLAIM — Made when a dividend has been paid to previous holder because stock not yet transferred to name of new owner.

DOW-JONES AVERAGE — An index of average prices based on the combined prices of 30 important and representative American industrial stocks which was first introduced by the Dow-Jones Company. Changes in the index are considered to be indicative of the whole industrial market. Indices are compiled by various stock exchanges to show the trend of the average price for various groups of stocks. For example, the Toronto Stock Exchange compiles indices for the industrial, base metal, gold and oil stocks.

ESCROWED SHARES — Shares deposited in trust pending fulfilment of certain conditions, and not ordinarily available to trading until released. (*See* also pooled shares).

EX-DIVIDEND — On stocks selling "ex-dividend" the seller retains the right to a pending dividend payment.

FIXED ASSETS — Possessions such as buildings, machinery and land which, as opposed to current assets, are unlikely to be converted into cash during the normal business cycle.

LIMIT ORDER — Must be executed at a specified price or better.

LONG POSITION — Securities owned outright or carried on margin.

MARGIN — Cash deposited with a broker as partial payment of purchase price for any type of listed stock. The stock is held by the broker as security for loan. Securities may be used as collateral in lieu of cash.

MARKET ORDER — An order to buy or sell at best price available. In absence of any specified price or limit an order is considered to be "at the market".

NET PROFIT — The profit that remains after deducting all charges, including taxes and bookkeeping charges such as depreciation.

NET WORTH — The difference between total assets and total liabilities.

ODD LOT – A block of shares which is less than the number specified as a board lot. *(See).* Usually, the cost is more than that for a board lot.

OPEN ORDER – Good until cancelled.

OPTION – Technically, a first refusal to purchase; (a) in mining finance it usually refers to an option on treasury shares at stated graded prices at stated time intervals as expressed in an effective contract; (b) an option to purchase a claim or group of claims, similarly bound by contract.

OVER-THE-COUNTER – A market for trading shares of companies which are not listed on a stock exchange either by choice or because they do not meet the listing requirements.

PAR, NO PAR – The par value of a stock is its stated face value in dollars or cents. Thus, if the capital consists of 3,000,000 shares each of $1 par value the authorized capital would be $3,000,000. No par value shares have no specified face value, but the total amount of authorized capital is set down in the company's charter.

POINT – This varies according to the stock exchange and the value of the stock. A point can be one dollar, one cent or expressed in one-eighths of a dollar.

POOLED SHARES – *See* **escrowed** shares.

PORTFOLIO – A list of assets.

PREFERRED SHARES – Shares of a limited liability company that rank ahead of common shares but after bonds in distribution of earnings or in claim to the company's assets in the event of liquidation. They pay a fixed dividend but normally do not have voting rights as with common shares.

PRICE-EARNINGS RATIO – Determined by dividing current price of stock by its net earnings per share for the year.

PROFIT AND LOSS STATEMENT – Also known as an **Income Statement,** in its simplest form means total profit = total revenue minus total costs.

PROXY – A power of attorney given by the shareholder so that his stock may be voted by his nominee(s) at meetings of shareholders.

PUT – An option to sell a stock at an agreed upon price within a specified time. The owner can present his put to the contracting broker at any time within the option period and compel him to buy the stock.

PYRAMIDING – The use of increased buying power to increase ownership arising from price appreciation.

RECORD DATE – The date by which a shareholder must be registered on the books of a company in order to receive a declared dividend, or to vote on company affairs.

RIGHTS – In finance, a certificated right to purchase treasury shares in stated quantities, prices, and time limits;

usually negotiable at a price which is related to the prices of the issue represented; also referred to as **warrants.** Rights and warrants can be bought and sold prior to their expiry date because not all shareholders wish to exercise their rights.

SHORT POSITION — When a broker sells stock the client is short the stock until he has made delivery of it to the broker.

SHORT SELLING — When stock is borrowed from a broker in order to sell it in the hope that it may be purchased at a lower price.

STOP-LOSS ORDER — A stop-loss order is an arrangement whereby a client gives his broker instructions to sell a stock if and when it drops to a specified figure on the market.

STREET CERTIFICATE — A certificate representing ownership in a specified number of shares which is registered in the name of some previous owner who has endorsed certificate so that it may be transferred to a new owner without referral to transfer agent.

SUBSIDIARY COMPANY — A company in which the majority of the shares of stock are held by another company, giving the control to the latter.

TRADING FLOOR — The portion of a stock exchange where shares are bought and sold.

TRADING POST — An area on the trading floor of a stock exchange where current stock prices are listed and where the floor traders (representatives of brokerage firms) meet to buy or sell the stocks listed at that particular post.

TRANSFER TAXES — The provinces of Ontario and Quebec impose a tax on stock transfers for transactions within the province. The tax is charged to the seller of the stock.

TREASURY SHARES — The unissued shares in a company's treasury.

UNDERWRITE — A firm commitment whereby a broker or other financing interest agrees to purchase a block of shares at a specified price.

VENDOR — The seller. In the case of mining companies the consideration paid for properties purchased is often a block of treasury shares. These shares are termed vendor shares and are normally **pooled** or **escrowed** (*See*).

WARRANT — *See* rights.

WORKING CAPITAL — The liquid resources a company has to meet the day to day expenses of operation. Defined as the excess of current assets over current liabilities.

WRITEOFFS — Amounts deducted from a company's reported profit for depreciation (*See*), depletion (*See*), or pre-production costs. Writeoffs are not an out-of-pocket expense but reduce the amount of taxable profit and are intended to reimburse the company for money previously expended.

YIELD — The current annual dividend rate expressed as a percentage of the current market price of the stock.

Index

Index continued

Index continued

Picture Credits

The publishers are deeply grateful for the splendid cooperation shown by a number of mining and oil companies which granted permission to reproduce many of the illustrations used in this volume. In particular, we wish to acknowledge the assistance provided by Inco Limited which supplied numerous photos; also, the generous help of the public relations departments of Falconbridge, Hudson Bay Mining, Rio Algom and Kidd Creek. A list of those firms and associations which provided pictures follows:

Barringer Research Ltd.

B.C. Coal Ltd.

Canadian Copper & Brass Development Association

Canadian Longyear Ltd.

Cominco Ltd.

Crone Geophysics Ltd.

Denison Mines Ltd.

Falconbridge Ltd.

Geometrics Services (Canada) Ltd.

Geonics Ltd.

George Hunter Photos

Suncor Inc.

Gulf Canada Ltd.

Heath & Sherwood Drilling

Hudson Bay Mining & Smelting Co.

Inco Limited

Imperial Oil Ltd.

Kidd Creek Mines Ltd.

McPhar Geophysics

Noranda Mines Ltd.

Ontario Department of Natural Resources, Division of Mines

Ontario Mining Association

Philips Electronics Ltd.

Rio Algom Mines

Scintrex Ltd.

Shell Canada Ltd.

J. K. Smit & Sons

The Toronto Stock Exchange

X-Ray Assay Laboratories

Zinc Institute Inc.

Printed in Canada by
NORGRAPHICS (CANADA) LIMITE